# The Old Gloucester
## The Story of a Cattle Breed

Adam Stout

ALAN SUTTON
1980

First published 1980 by

Alan Sutton Publishing Limited
17a Brunswick Road
Gloucester, GL1 1HG

**British Library Cataloguing in Publication Data**

Stout, Adam
   The Old Gloucester.
   1. Old Gloucester Cattle - History
   I. Title
   636.2'2      SF199.04

   ISBN 0 904387 42 9

Typesetting and origination by
Alan Sutton Publishing Limited
Set in Times Roman 11/13
Printed in Great Britain by
Redwood Burn Limited
Trowbridge & Esher

# Contents

|  | Page |
|---|---|
| Preface and Acknowledgements | 5 |
| Introduction:<br>Description of the Breed | 8 |
| In the Beginning:<br>Origins of the Breed | 11 |
| 'A choice Breed' | 18 |
| Losing to the Longhorn:<br>The Late Eighteenth Century | 28 |
| The Nineteenth Century | 39 |
| Interest at Last:<br>The First Gloucester Cattle Society | 51 |
| Renaissance | 70 |
| The Glamorgan Connection | 79 |
| The Jenner Connection | 84 |
| Bibliography | 86 |
| Notes | 91 |
| Index | 93 |

*To Tappo & Totty*

# Preface and Acknowledgements

My interest in the Gloucester breed dates from about 1973, and I soon afterwards realised how little work had been done on the breed's past, and how large the gaps in our knowledge were — gaps that I have attempted to fill with this brief study. Unlike most breed histories it is not the study of a success story — more of the remarkable tenacity and faith of a handful of stalwarts, who refused to follow those fads of fashion that dethroned the Gloucester, Longhorn and Shorthorn in turn, and preferred to stick to their old and tried county breed, which continued to serve them well; although as a 'national' breed the Gloucester has been in commercial cold storage for two centuries. Thus this book is essentially the story of a livestock-breeding enigma, of a breed which refused to die; of its early prosperity, its decline and the process of preservation.

> 'The Old Gloucester breed has been a-dying for so long that its very tenacity of life leads one to hope against all the evidence that it may eventually survive'[1]

The breed's example stands as a warning to the currently successful breeds, and as a blueprint for survival for the numerically small breeds of livestock. I hope that this book will prove to be of value to those interested in the history of Gloucestershire as well, for dairy farming is still the county's chief industry, and its fame was built on the milk of the Gloucester.

My greatest debt is, of course, to the Gloucester Cattle Society, who collectively commissioned this book and individually have always been enthusiastic, helpful and generous; but I must point out, however, that all opinions expressed in this book are my own, as are the errors, and do not necessarily represent Society policy or viewpoints. Lack of space has ruled out extensive footnotes, but a fully annotated copy has been deposited at Gloucestershire Records Office. I owe much to the patience and tolerance of the staff there, and at the City Library in Brunswick Road.

Mr H.W.G. Elwes of Colesbourne Park kindly allowed me to make extensive reference to his grandfather's records at Colesbourne, and to copy some of his considerable collection of photographs. Miss Alex and the late Miss Ella Dowdeswell of Wick Court have given me much help and information concerning their herd, Earl Bathurst generously gave me some photographs of his grandfather's cattle, and I am indebted to Messrs. S.C. Andrews, N.J.B. Cripps, Arthur B. Lloyd-Baker, Gerald Yorke, Eric Freeman, Chris Peachey, Joe Henson, Robin Otter, Earl St Aldwyn, Baron Cromwell, Sir Jeffrey Darrell and Sir Christopher Codrington for information concerning their own and their relatives' herds; the staff at the 'Citizen', 'Cotswold Life', 'Gloucestershire Life', and 'Farmers' Weekly' for further information and pictures. I am also very grateful to the staff at the following libraries for their help: University of Reading, Museum of English Rural Life, Milk Marketing Board, Ministry of Agriculture, Windsor Castle, Guildhall, Westminster and Amersham. The Vicar of Boddington, Rev. Homfray, kindly searched his parish registers for references to aid me in my search for Long of Boddington (p. 35), and I must thank all those who have advised me with regard to publishing the book, particularly Mr Roger Farrand and Miss Moira Fisher of

Academic Press; and my mother, Mrs Dorothy Stout, for typing out the original drafts of the book from my illegible scrawl. But unquestionably my greatest debt of all is to Society Secretary Charles Martell and his family, for their unflagging interest and support, for much valuable information, for proof-reading and a hundred other things; not least for letting me billet myself at their home during my frequent visits to Gloucestershire.

# Introduction
## Description of the Breed

The Old Gloucester, Gloucestershire or Gloucester is one of the oldest dairy breeds in the country; today it is one of the rarest.

The breed is unusual amongst British cattle in that it has altered little in its outward characteristics for two centuries at least, and the breed Society's 'points of the breed' as drawn up in 1919 are as applicable to today's cattle as to those of the eighteenth century. Marshall's description of a prime Gloucester cow in the 1780's (see p. 37) should be regarded as a breed prototype, but his comments on the breed in general are equally as valuable:

> 'the head mostly small; neck long; shoulder fine; and all of them generally clean. The carcase mostly long, with the ribs full and the barrel large in proportion to the chest and hind-quarters. The huckle of due width; but the nache frequently narrow. The bone, in general, fine; the hide thin and the hair short. The characteristic colour, dark red — provincially brown — with the face and neck inclining to black; and with an irregular line of white along the back. The horns fine and rather long; but, in some individuals, placed awkwardly high on the forehead, and near at the roots; in others, however, they stand low and wide; winding with a double bend, in the middle-horn manner'.

Today the Gloucester is similar in size to the Ayrshire or Dairy Shorthorn (about 850 lbs) but in 1807 Rudge found the average weight to be between 640 and 720 lbs, rising to

960 lbs on good feed. Early crosses with the Longhorn produced a cow weighing 12½ cwt, and with the Hereford 14½ cwt; but the salient fact to emerge from both accounts is that the Gloucester was already an excellent dairy cow —

'their bags are thin in flesh and large, yielding a good deal of milk, and continuing for a long time, when on good keep'.[2]

The Gloucester was always a heavy milker, and was already yielding about 500 gallons in Marshalls' day, and the average yield of seventeen recorded lactations in the period 1920-1940 was 7,419 lbs, at least 200 gallons above the national average. One cow, the only Gloucester ever owned by Mr S.C. Andrews, of Sutton St Nicholas, Herefordshire, yielded 10,999½ lbs in 1927. Had the Gloucester but benefited from the investment and technique that has been dedicated to other breeds during the last half-century, there is little doubt that it would have become as good a dairy breed as any — and perhaps better than many!

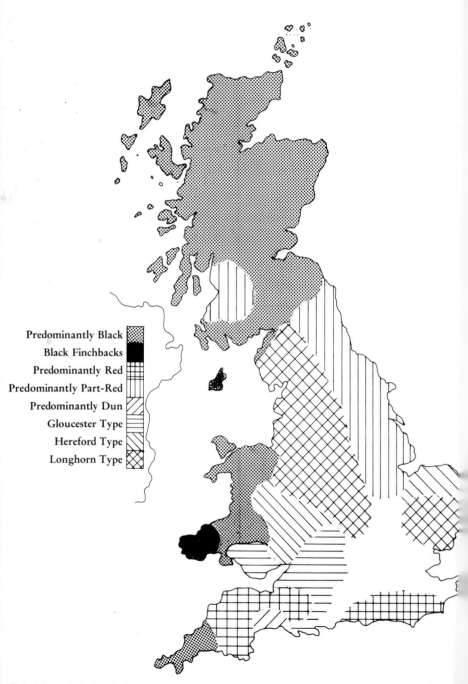

| | |
|---|---|
| Predominantly Black | |
| Black Finchbacks | |
| Predominantly Red | |
| Predominantly Part-Red | |
| Predominantly Dun | |
| Gloucester Type | |
| Hereford Type | |
| Longhorn Type | |

Britain's cattle before Bakewell: approximate distribution by colour c. 1750, based on the Board of Agriculture County Reports 1792-1815 and the work of Marshall and Young

# In the Beginning: Origins of the Breed

Thirteen thousand years ago the world's longest-lived art exhibition was mounted by the neolithic hunters of south-western France, in a cave at Lascaux. Amongst the detailed and vivid drawings of the animals they knew and hunted is a fine-boned, 'finchbacked' cow with a brown body, a dark head and middle-length horns; and allowing for artistic license she might well have been a Gloucester — but she has been identified as a member of that great primeval cattle race, the 'Aurochs', or 'Bos Primigenius', at that period to be found throughout the temperate world, and not finally extinct until the seventeenth century. Perhaps it would be going a bit far to prescribe such an ancestry for the breed, but there is plenty of room for speculation!

Tracing cattle breed origins is an emotive business and a highly inconclusive one, for the word 'breed' in its present usage only dates back some two hundred years at the outside. Before that date cattle were distinguished by their county of origin, a vague practice which did not matter much when several counties shared the same breed, but could be of great significance if they did not. Greater brains than mine have devoted long hours and many pages towards solving the mystery of cattle breed origins; so I will restrict myself to defining a 'breed' as being a group of animals bred in one area, and which, through a common aim on the part of the breeder (meat, milk, traction, wool), through climate, geology and land use, and sometimes through isolation, gradually achieved a degree of genetic uniformity. This provided the raw material for the 'Improvers' of the eighteenth and nineteenth century, who then established inflexible uniformity and the prototypes of today's breeds.

Breed fervour aroused — and arouses — loyalty and devotion even more strongly than patriotism, and any study into breed origins is hampered by two centuries of enthusiastic mythology and synthetic ancestries:

> 'It was as though a pure descent from some mythical, indigenous Old Adam of a beast was a sine qua non of a perfect performance in the pail or upon the butchers block'.[3]

To throw some light on the obscure origins of the Gloucester it is necessary to look to the agricultural authors of the eighteenth and nineteenth centuries, when — by and large — such breeds as there were, were still much the same as they had been for centuries.

My first proposition is that, at some point in time, there existed a vaguely homogenous 'Severnside' breed, or rather type, which was distinguished from the cattle to the west and south by a colour range from middle red to deep brown, and a variable amount of white markings; cattle of this description were to be found from Montgomery to Glamorgan, and from Hereford to Somerset and Wiltshire in the late eighteenth century.

The red element in this 'breed' certainly shares a common ancestor with the red of the Devon, but the mahogany colour of the Gloucester is unique today. The Sussex breed approaches Gloucester colouring most nearly, and the brown element was present in the Lincoln Red of 1790, to judge from Stubbs' famous 'Lincolnshire Ox'; this helps to explain the similarities between the cattle of Gloucestershire, Somerset and Lincolnshire that

Gervase Markham noticed in his 'Cheap and Good Husbandry' (1623) and as he goes on to call these breeds 'generally blood-red in colour' (almost certainly an exaggeration and probably merely hearsay — p. 22 ), there does seem to be an implicit link-up between my 'Severnside' breed and the other old red breeds of Britain. Once believed to have been introduced into Britain by the Saxons, it now seems likely that these red cattle are the remnants of an old landrace breed, perhaps the domesticated descendants of the Aurochs. The mahogany hue was probably the result of crossing between these 'indigenous' types and the Welsh drovers' black cattle in the Middle Ages; although Ayres suggests an even earlier cross with the small, fine-boned black Bos Longifrons cattle, remains of which have been found at Gloucester and Glastonbury, both dairying regions of ancient reputation. Either theory would account for both the finer bone structure of the Gloucester, relative to the other breeds in my 'Severnside' composite, and its darker colouring.

The finchback, or white dorsal stripe, is the breed's other colour characteristic, and was shared, in varying degrees, by all the cattle in the 'Severnside' group. This, too, may well have been present for thousands of years and have been a part of the landrace's colour marking legacy, itself descended from the Aurochs. That the Aurochs carried this factor is proven by the Lascaux painting, and at least two Aurochs skeletons have been found in Gloucestershire; but there are literally dozens of alternative suggestions as to the origins of the Gloucestershire finchback, and I shall here comment on the more probable!

A Norman origin was hinted at by Lawrence in 1805, and seized upon and developed by Davies in 1814, who suggested that the finchback was brought to this part of Britain by Robert Fitzhamon in the early twelfth century to his vast estates in Gloucestershire and in Glamorgan, which county he himself conquered. There is not one shred of evidence to support this particular claim, however appealing it may be, but it is true that the finchback pattern occurs occasionally in the modern Normande and Parthenaise breeds, and in view of the three centuries of sporadic English occupation, and the trading links that grew up, it is quite possible that cattle were imported from France; Earl Berkeley, for example, had his own 'barke or ship' in about 1300

> 'for the importation back of forren wines and wares, needful for his own use'.[4]

Robert Trow Smith, although a justly famous livestock historian, had a tendency to ascribe all white colour marking to Dutch importations, on the most tenuous of evidence in many cases; for whilst it seems geographically and historically probable that Dutch influence was strong in Eastern England, the only known introduction of Dutch blood into the 'Severnside' breeds was a few red cows to Lord Scudamore's herd in Hereford in the mid-seventeenth century; there is no reference as to their having been finch-backed; anyway it is believed that Scudamore selected these cattle because of their similarity to his breed at home.[5]

Altogether more probable, as a source for the finchback factor in the region, is Scandinavia. The cattle of Norway and Sweden have traditionally shown a considerable amount of finching, and even today the Norweigan Red, which has now practically replaced the original breeds, has a large proportion of finchbacks. Cattle-breeding was a mainstay of the Viking economy, and although I can find no proof that cattle were ever brought to Britain, they certainly went to Iceland. There is strong circumstantial evidence that they were, however, both in the occurence of the Norse polled factor in the breeds of the North Sea Littoral, and the finchback factor in the regions occupied by the Vikings — notably the Shetlands, a Norse colony until the fourteenth century, but also in Lancashire and Ireland. There are scant traces of Norse settlement in Gloucestershire, although there are more in Glamorgan, but the region was on the boundary of the Norse lands in England from the ninth century, (a point emphasised by the fact that it was on Alney Island, just outside Gloucester, that the two Kings met in 1016 to divide up the country.) It is quite likely, therefore, that the 'Severnside' finchbacks have a common ancestry with the Lancashire Longhorn in some Viking-based finchback landrace which spread wherever the Norsemen did.

Finally I must break up my 'Severnside' conglomerate and try to establish which of its constituent breeds came first. The Glamorgan (see Appendix I) was almost identical to the Gloucester, and as the cattle of Monmouthshire were labelled as being part Glamorgan and part Gloucester in 1860, I think it reasonable to state that at one time the breeds were one and the same thing, perhaps with the addition of the Hereford, which was not always white-faced but was, in the eighteenth century, often fully finchbacked (now the finchback is restricted to a white line on the shoulder), and noticeably longer in the head and better in the pail than their descendants today; whilst the other 'Severnside' breeds were modified more extensively by crossings with neighbouring breeds; and that the distinction between the Gloucester and the Glamorgan only arose when the Glamorgan was developed as a beef animal, while the Gloucester had been bred for the dairy from very early on. But great controversy has surrounded the question of which end, geographically speaking, of this 'breed', came first. Norse settlement is marginally better documented in Glamorgan than in Gloucestershire, but as seen above this does not automatically mean that any Norse contribution to the breed's genetic stock had to originate in Glamorgan. The only other Welsh breed regularly to show finching was the famous old Castlemartin breed of Pembrokeshire, and it is highly unlikely that the finchback, in view of its prevalence in England, came from the west and not the east — although of course this is not to deny that the drovers' stock played a major role in establishing some of the other breed characteristics.

Agricultural innovation appears to have followed a generally east-west pattern, hardly surprising considering the poverty of much of Wales at that time; one example of this is to be found in the spread of the hoop-raved farm wagon (p. 25 ). There is also what could be a significant reference in an observation made by Lisle in 1707:

> 'In South Wales, as in Glamorganshire, they have thin-hided cattle, which are much on the red and brown colour, and they get their breed from Gloucestershire'.[6]

Marshall, writing eighty years later, makes no reference to this trade, which may therefore have been restricted to a few progressive farmers; on the other hand it could be that Lisle was writing about the tail-end of a centuries-old practice. Marshall was, however, the first of many to note a similarity between my 'Severnside' breeds and the Welsh cattle, and from this Lawrence developed the traditional theory of the origins of the finchback, which was in turn converted to definite fact by Davies and Youatt, who bolstered up the statement with the Fitzhamon connection; the whole myth was later used to help Badminton claim responsibility for creating the Gloucester breed, and has been used in countless references to the origins of the breed, a good example of the bovine hagiography that dogs the steps of a breed historian!

The ramifications of breed origins are endless, and although I have attempted to give a reasonably balanced summary of what evidence there is and how it could be interpreted, in such dearth of fact and surfeit of opinion every man has to be his own expert.

ow breed by F.A. Davies, Pinckney, Wilts., whose *Ladyswood* herd, dispersed in )20, was one of the Badminton satellite herds that paved the way for the creation f the breed society.

# 'A Choice Breed'

Dairy cattle were to be found in the Vale of Berkeley as early as 1300; and whilst it is quite possible that Marshall may have been able to recognise in these cattle the breed he knew five hundred years later, it must be remembered that Gloucester was already becoming established as a major droving centre, and that there was bound to be at least some dilution of the native breed through crossing with Welsh cattle.

The jurassic lower lias which lies below the Vales of Gloucester and Berkeley is part of a band of this rock-type which stretches from Leicestershire to Lyme Regis, and is everywhere characterised by a history of dairying. Cheese-making in Gloucestershire dates back to the thirteenth century at least, and throughout its history Gloucester cheese has been synonymous with the Gloucester cow, but a word of caution is needed here; for cheese in the Middle Ages was often made from goat's and sheep milk, and we know that ewes were being milked at Minchinhampton and Berkeley in the early fourteenth century. But the early development of the Cotswold wool industry conceivably meant that the sheep population, being bred for centuries as high-grade wool producers, experienced a decline in their dairying abilities, and the onus thus put upon the cow population would then have meant that stock were early on selected and bred for the dairy: this is pure hypothesis however. Certainly a twenty-cow herd at Tidenham was selling large quantities of cheese in the late thirteenth century, and from this date the leather trade at Gloucester began to expand rapidly; but this might, of course, only be implying an expanding trade in droving animals as opposed to those bred and reared locally.

A seventeen-cow herd belonging to the nuns of Caen (Normandy) at Minchinhampton was producing 445 cheeses and 121 lbs of butter during the summer of 1307, at the rate of two cheeses per day from May to July, one a day in August and one every two days in September, after which time any milk was looked upon as a bonus — so presumably these cows had a five or six month summer lactation. Some attempt can be made to estimate the average yield of these cows during their brief spell in milk, for in 1330 the standard cheese sizes were 8 lbs, 4½ lbs and 3 lbs — an average weight of about 5 lbs. Assuming a conversion factor of 10 lbs milk : 1 lb cheese, and that the calf was reared and the butter made from skim milk after the cheese had been made, a lactation yield of about 130 gallons is indicated, which was a fairly average one for the time. This figure is very tentative, however, and ignores the presence of 1886 sheep on the estate despite a reference to ewes being milked; so it must not be taken as absolute.[7]

The Earls of Berkeley not only kept cattle at this time, but also seem to have made rudimentary attempts to improve their management. Earl Maurice in 1269 gave the freemen in his manors the right to graze their cattle and pigs with his own herds within the Hundred of Berkeley; and if foreign blood ever was introduced, such practice would have widely distributed it within a very few years. His son Thomas, Earl from 1281-1321, was an efficient dairy farmer 'in soe much as every dayes and everye meale's milke of every cow was rate'd and proportioned to the inferior servant, as what quantity of butter and cheese might be raised there from, according to the diverse Seasons of summer and winter, the pasture where they fed and the like'.

The livestock at Berkeley during the earldom of the second Earl Thomas (1326-1361) appears to have been considered superior to that of his neighbours, for he stocked his manors with 'his owne oxen, kine, sheep, swine and other cattle', and in the late fourteenth century his descendant was sending his cattle elsewhere for fattening, which his seventeenth century biographer could not understand,

'he having so rich and sweet feeding grounds for grass and hay more neare unto his Castle'.[8]

Perhaps the home farms were overstocked, but it is probably too far-fetched to deduce from this snippet that at that date the Berkeleys were already separating dairy from beef cattle; at all events they appear to have been a very progressive farming family.

Cheese and butter markets were established at both Chipping Sodbury and Gloucester in the early thirteenth century, and the annual farming event at Gloucester — the Barton Fair, still held on 28 September, was by the eighteenth century the principal cheese fair in the county; it was held near the junction of what is now Wellington Street and Barton Street. Gloucester had also acquired a permanent cheese market at the Kings' Board, in Westgate Street, by 1498; and Leland, thirty-seven years later, found that Alney Island, just to the west of the town, was

'al very goodly medow ground . . . cheese there made is in great price'.[9]

Amongst the documents relating to the Abbey of Gloucester at this time is a list of rules and regulations for the use of the Abbey's bailiffs:

> '. . . Each ox stall to be of equal length, containing sufficient hay for each team of oxen or horses every night. . . .'
> 'no useless or unprofitable beasts to be kept throughout the winter to the waste of hay and fodder. . . .'
> 'All calves . . . to be marked'.
> 'No steward to ride any bullock belonging to the (abbey) Court at any time'. . . .

— perhaps the earliest reference to Gloucestershire stockmanship! In 1536 the Abbot owned '12 oxen, 16 kyne and one bulle', obviously a dairy herd from later references to '2 pannes and 2 cheesevattes'.[10] Milk and cheese were by now being produced in sufficient quantities for a canny farmer at Sherborne, on the Cotswolds, to offer his haymakers

> 'milk to the value of 4d and cheese to the value of 1s. 1d.'

fifty years before. He cannot have been very popular, for in most places fieldworkers slaked their thirst with cider and beer![11]

Cheesemaking and cattle breeding have a long recorded history in Gloucestershire, and as initially a breed was the product of its usage, the conformation of the Gloucester as we know her today was probably well-developed already; but the question of colour is altogether more complex and less well documented.

The Manorial Court Rolls contain certain indications amongst the receipts for *heriot* — a feudal practice which involved the surrender of a tenant's 'best beast' on his death or marriage, and which, incidentally, presumably led to a concentration of the best animals on the big estates; the Churchdown Court Roll for the decade 1538-

1548, for example, lists seven 'red' and three 'yellow' animals surrendered to the Lord of the Manor. In 1623 Markham described the cattle of Gloucestershire as 'blood red', comparing them with those of Lincolnshire — which he elsewhere describes as having white markings. Perhaps he was merely remarking on the dairy properties of the breed, as he also quotes the ancient maxim that 'the Red cow giveth the best milk'. Brown and white cattle were being sold at Gloucester Market in 1653, and red cattle at Newnham a year later, so red certainly was not the only coat colour of the early Gloucester.

The brown factor may have been an indigenous one, dating from the dawn of time; it may have been the result of crossing native cattle with black beasts from Wales en route for the south-east; or it may simply have been an aberration of the red — hinting at a common ancestor with the Devon; it is the yellow (or dun) and the white that are the most interesting. Both are recessive colours and can easily be crossed out by a few generations of cattle of darker colouring, with only the occasional throwback to hint as to its ever having existed; to my knowledge neither colour was ever well established in this region. There are several early references to white cattle in Wales however, and it is quite likely that these colours arrived with the drovers. And they are unlikely to have been whole colours either — such brief descriptions are part of the farmer's verbal shorthand today, as for instance a mainly black Friesian is referred to as 'black' as a simple means of identification. Thus it does not mean that the finchback was rare — on the contrary it could have been so common as to have escaped comment. In the absence of any conclusive evidence it is probably reasonable to say that the sixteenth-century Gloucester had its finchback, and a range of colours from Hereford red to Sussex brown; and that gradual selection for the mahogany colour today so typical of the breed had established the colour well enough by the early 1700's for the 'Gloucester brown kind' to have been considered as a distinct type. The two colours probably existed side by side throughout Gloucestershire and Herefordshire for centuries, and were not separated for breeding purposes until the seventeenth century; it is perhaps significant that in 1653-54 Nathaniel Clutterbuck distinguished between his brown heifers and his red bullock.[12]

The colour of these cattle may be in doubt, but there is no doubt that by the end of the sixteenth century there were plenty of them in the breed's heartland:

> 'The Soile is for the most part bountefull; ritch in pasture and meadow, fruitful in procreation of divers and different kinds of trees . . . the lowe and fat grounds doe yield such abundance of pasture for kyne and oxen, as sufficeth the greediness of those beasts, and the covetousness of their owners'.

Cattle were so numerous, indeed, that the Vicar of Berkeley received up to 130 calves a year in tithes alone, and this despite the fact that farmers who had less than six calves a year paid nothing.[13] Herd sizes, to judge from a random sample of ten inventories taken between 1518 and 1713, varied on average from nine to eighteen cows; and a breakdown of the manorial herd at Horsley in 1613 shows that there were ten cows, five two-year-olds, fifteen yearlings and seven calves, besides an eight-ox team and two fatting steers. This appears to have been slightly above the average size, and there must have been hundreds of farmers in the Vale of Berkeley with less than six calves per year.

The beginning of the eighteenth century found the Gloucester reaching its zenith. Gloucesters were to be found the Monmouthshire to Devon, and Lisle paid the breed its first compliment, albeit backhanded, in about 1707:

> 'Mr Raymond . . . says that if you have yearling heifers, and a yearling bull, of the Gloucester brown kind for a choice breed, you must often by renewing, or keeping-up the breed, by buying on of those yearling bulls; otherwise the breed will soon degenerate'.

This could be taken as casting aspersions on the virility of an older Gloucester bull; but more likely it was already apparent that the breed did not take kindly to outcrossing.

Double Gloucester too was now reaching its peak of popularity. Defoe, writing about Gloucestershire and North Wiltshire in 1724, found other cheese masquerading as Gloucester:

> 'the cheese they make is excellent, and is eaten greener than that in Cheshire. Of this a vast Quantity is every week sent up to London, where though it is called Gloucester cheese, yet the greater Part of it comes from Wiltshire; the Gloucester cheese being more generally carried to Bristol or Bath, where a very great Quantity is consumed, as well by the Inhabitants of those two populous Cities, as in Exportation to our West India Colonies'.

Defoe goes on to say that so popular was the local green cream cheese in London that demand exceeded supply during May and June, the months when it was made. Gloucestershire bacon was in London rated second only to Hampshire, and large numbers of baconers were fattened on whey and skimmed milk — one obvious connection between the Gloucester cow and the Gloucester Old Spot pig.

As Defoe mentioned, Double Gloucester was already crossing the Atlantic; Carolina is one known recipient, and another was Williamsburg in Virginia.

There is some evidence to show that the Gloucester cow itself was exported to New England, for cattle are known to have been introduced there by the early settlers, some of whom came from Gloucestershire. The 'Colonial Williamsburg Foundation', which has restored the town to its pre-Revolution state, were at one time considering importing Gloucester semen in a scheme to 'reconstruct' the contemporary breeds of livestock.

Back home the Gloucester was already expanding outside its native county. 'Wiltshire Loaf', Wiltshire's local cheese, was prepared almost identically to that of Gloucestershire, demonstrating a similarity in dairying technique that was reflected in the county's cattle population. Aubrey in his 'Natural History of Wiltshire' (1687) found that coat colours ranged from black to deep red, often with white markings; and despite outcrossing on a massive scale the influence of the Gloucester was still apparent in the mid-nineteenth century. Gloucester-type cattle were to be found on the fringes of Dartmoor, and Dorset's 'Blue Vinny' cheese was originally made from the milk of Gloucester cows summering near Sherborne; Gloucesters were even to be found amongst the dairy cattle of Cambridgeshire.

Oxen rather than horses were being used in Gloucestershire from an early date, and teams of Gloucester oxen were to be found in Essex and Surrey in the mid-eighteenth century. Centuries of preferential breeding for the dairy probably led to a bone structure too fine for draught work however; at any rate the Gloucester ox was being rapidly eclipsed even in his own county by the Hereford and the Devon by the end of the century.

A curious connection between Gloucester oxen and the carts they pulled is to be found in the zoomorphic, similarities between the old Gloucestershire, Wiltshire and Glamorgan hoop-raved farm wagons; their front siderails curve upwards like the horns of an ox, and the Glamorgan wagon further possessed 'balusters', furry decoration on the front board which has been taken as representing the ox's hairy fringe. The 'horns' of the wagon are surprisingly similar to those of the Gloucester cow; and by a striking coincidence the distribution of this form of 'panel-sided bow-wagon' almost exactly paralleled the distribution of the Gloucester and Glamorgan breeds; and further, the wagon occurs 'in a greatly degenerated form' in Pembrokeshire, home of the finchbacked Castlemartin breed. Whilst it would be a bit far-fetched to interpret this as conclusive proof of the origin of the Welsh finchback, it is at least further proof of the strong agricultural interchange between Gloucestershire and South Wales.

The pinnacle of Gloucestershire's fame as a dairy county was reached in the mid-eighteenth century; and the breed could have looked out for a prosperous future at the hands of the great cattle improvers but for a double disaster that made the Gloucester rare within fifty years.

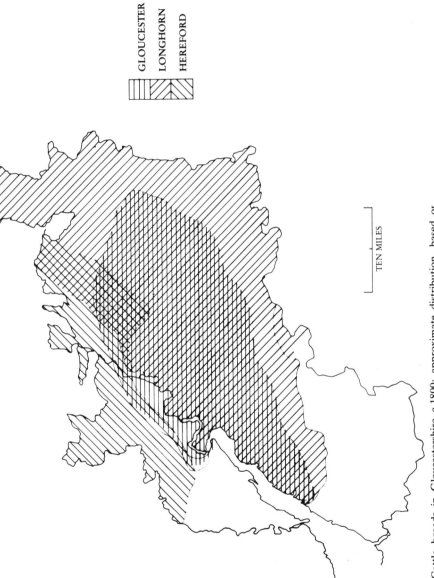

GLOUCESTER

LONGHORN

HEREFORD

TEN MILES

Cattle breeds in Gloucestershire c.1800: approximate distribution, based on Marshall, Turner and Youatt. Shading shows relative density

## Losing to the Longhorn: The Late Eighteenth Century

The first of these disasters, which almost certainly triggered off the second, was the great rinderpest epidemic of 1745-56. It was only one of a series of 'Cattle Plagues', and was by no means the last, but its severity and length made it stand apart. There are no accurate figures for the total death toll, but it must have been millions, to judge from the fact that in 1748 alone the Government ordered the slaughter of 80,000 cattle in a bid to stem the disease; Lincolnshire lost 100,000 cattle in 1746, and Cheshire 30,000 between October 1750 and May 1751. The protracted length of the disease is usually attributed to widespread evasion of the Government's compulsory slaughter programme, understandable when its success was not proven and compensation was less than a third of the market value.

Unfortunately there is not even an estimate for the death toll in Gloucestershire. The disease first arrived there early in 1748, although on Government orders inspectors had been appointed a year earlier, and the first outbreak seems to have been at Forthampton, near Tewkesbury. Again under orders from London, the county Justices took drastic action:

> 'It is ordered by this Court that no fair or market for cattle, either fat or lean, to be from henceforth held in any Town, Parish or Place within the said County'. [14]

The disease appears to have abated by 1752, for that Easter the authorities had to introduce fresh restrictions on stock movement following outbreaks in Ashchurch and Beckford, again in the north of the county.

The greatest effect of this nationwide calamity was to leave a vacuum in cattle breeding on an unprecedented scale; some areas turned over wholesale to arable farming. After previous epidemics, presumably, numbers had slowly increased back to normal through natural increase; but this time there was an alternative: the Longhorn.

Robert Bakewell has for long been considered to be virtually the creator of this breed, but in reality it had already spread from its original heartland of Lancashire to become the commonest breed in the Midlands centuries before Bakewell was born; and he was preceded in his attempts at amelioration by Webster at Canley in the 1730's, and possibly before that by Sir Thomas Gresley. Webster had reintroduced Lancashire blood into the Midlands Longhorn, and achieved a considerable degree of recognition; all that the breed required was a setback to cattle-breeding elsewhere to become established on a national scale — and the epidemic came at the perfect time. By the 1760's the Longhorn had become a common sight in dairies throughout the country, and good dairy stock was already becoming hard to find and expensive.

In Gloucestershire at least, the situation was made that much easier for the Longhorn by the fact that several years of high prices for dairy produce had encouraged Vale farmers to replace their young stock with milch cows in order to cash in fully on the boom — and the Longhorn thus gained a foothold in this best of all cheesemaking counties; for the Gloucestershire farmers were happy to leave the work of breeding to the men of the Midland counties, and Staffordshire in particular. Once the publicity machine of Bakewell began to have effect, in the

1770's, even Gloucestershire Longhorns began to acquire a market value well above their commercial worth, and the 'foothold' became a flood. Suddenly everybody who was anybody had to have Longhorns: an element of fashion and oneupmanship came into the picture — best illustrated by the Rollright Longhorn Sale in 1791, just over the border in Oxfordshire, where the prices paid have since become legendary. But this, of course, is not the whole story.

The Longhorn had a higher butterfat than the Gloucester, but the Gloucester gave more milk and the cheese produced per cow was on a par; a dairying explanation for the 'invasion' is not satisfactory, but a beef one is. The Longhorn, although primarily a dairy breed, was beefier than the Gloucester ever was. It is much the same story today, with the minor dairy breeds pitted against the Friesian, whose succinct motto 'Single Purpose — Dual Result' sums up that breed's success in recent years. The Gloucester, like the Ayrshire today, was already a specialist dairy breed — an unpardonable crime in those days of pedigree beef breeding. I cannot accept today's argument that the Gloucester has always been a dual purpose breed — at some distant point in the past, certainly, 'Gloucester' beef was consumed because there was no other, but of course the only beef eaten in the Middle Ages came from cattle too old to work; the Hereford supplied the county with beef from an early date. This is not to say that the breed today is not dual purpose, but what beefiness there is in the Gloucester is the result of outcrossing earlier this century. It is no coincidence that the Gloucester ox was rapidly replaced by the Hereford and the Devon once their draught potential was fully appreciated by the Gloucestershire arable men.

The breed was denigrated in the late eighteenth century for its fineness of bone and its meagre dewlap — 'deficiency of chine' — which gave the breed 'an awkward and uncouth appearance' in comparison with such breeds as the Hereford; but both points are today highly sought-after by pedigree dairy breeders:

> 'Every variety of cattle has a tendency to degenerate, and each appears to have its peculiar propensity in degenerating. Thus the Gloucester breed became, under neglect, narrow in the chest, light in the hindquarters, and long upon the legs'.

The Gloucester's horns and head were also described as 'illshaped' in 1776, but this did not stop them from being 'amongst the best dairy cattle in the country'. Thirteen years later, Marshall wrote that 'for dairy cows I have not, in my judgement, seen a better form', and 'one of the handsomest and most desirable dairy cows I have yet seen was a Gloucester.'[15]

The Longhorn takeover was not completely troublefree, however, and there remained a number of dairy farmers who continued to keep the Gloucester and to preserve its purity; one experienced dairymaid found that

> 'the North-country cows neither milk so well nor fat so well as the true dark-brown Gloucestershire breed'.

There was even a slight reversal, for in 1783 'it was said that the North-country cows were losing ground; and that the old stock were coming again into esteem' in the Vale of Berkeley at least. But this was only a temporary setback:

> 'In 1783, dairies were mostly of the Gloucestershire breed; in some, a mixture of the Longhorned sort was observable; — and in the lower vale, a few dairies were mostly of that breed. Now (1788) few dairies are left without admixture; and, even in the upper vale, are some entire dairies of the Longhorned breed. In general, however, they are an unsightly mixture of the two species; with, not unfrequently, a third sort, a mongrel kind, reared from an awkward cross between them. In the fairs

and markets of the vale, scarcely any other than the north country sort and this mule breed are to be seen'.[16]

The above and many of the previous quotations in this chapter were written by William Marshall (1745-1815), one of the most perceptive and thorough of the generation of writers to emerge from the Agricultural Revolution. Marshall's 'Rural Economy of Gloucestershire', first published in 1789, is the result of two extended visits to the county, in 1783 and 1788; and scattered within its pages is the best and most thorough survey of the breed ever to be made. It is largely to Marshall that I owe the following account of dairy herd management at the time.

About thirty per cent of the Gloucestershire calf crop was reared for milk production. Calving was generally planned for about Christmas time, and the calves were left on their dams for about three days, until the colostrum — locally known as 'boister milk' — was finished; they were then reared on hot skim milk, which was gradually replaced by linseed jelly containing increasing amounts of oat or barley flour, until at about three weeks they were fully weaned onto hay and cereals; they were housed in purpose-built slatted calf pens known as 'stages'. At four to five months old, they were turned onto the best of the spring grass, and the following winter they were fed on prime hay; but for their second year they were turned out onto any convenient rough ground during the summer, and only fed straw during the winter. The heifers ran with the bull during the next summer, to calve down the following spring at three years old.

Milking cows were turned out at the beginning of May, onto the same set of fields that they were to graze all summer — a practice today known as 'set stocking'. They were dried off during the winter, and fed on straw alone until they were 'steamed-up' on hay a month or so before calving. Winter management depended on the primary function of the farm, however, and on an all-dairy farm they would be out-wintered, or at best loose-housed; but they would then be fed hay instead of straw.

The average yield per lactation was about 500 gallons, already comfortably above the 'national average', but irrelevant in those days as most of the milk was processed. In practice the Gloucester was merely on a par with the Longhorn, for both produced about 3 cwt of cheese per annum because of the Longhorn's higher butterfat. The Gloucester today, however, has a very good butterfat record, which may be the result of the considerable crossing which took place between the two breeds (see p. 31). At all events the potential high yield of the Gloucester, like that of the Suffolk Dun, was not appreciated until half a century too late to save the breed commercially. Five or six lactations was considered a good span for a dairy cow, after which they were sent for slaughter; but if a Gloucester was ever sold in milk, it was always when she was freshly calved, and with the calf at foot — when they fetched only four-fifths the price of equivalent Longhorn stock.

Gloucestershire sainfoin was in very high repute nationally — a sample sent to Essex in the 1760's yielded 'over three tuns to the acre' — and good crops of clover and ryegrass were produced from the richer soils; but it was the ancient, undeveloped permanent pastures with their crops of fleabane, devilsbit, resharrow and rushes that were said to produce the best quality cheese, so there was little inducement to improve their quality. Herd sizes had doubled from about nine to eighteen cows (p. 23) in the sixteenth and seventeenth centuries to about twenty to thirty cows which perhaps reflects the growth in the Gloucestershire cheese industry in this period; but management remained fairly mediocre, and stocking rates low. The owner of a 40-60 cow herd in 1765 could manage

no greater profit than £2 per cow per year, which, if it can
be equated to the modern 'margin over concentrates', was
at best a quarter of her market value at the time. Marshall
put the stocking rate at about four acres per 'cow unit', and
using this figure estimated the dairy cow population of the
Vale of Berkeley at 7,300. It should be noted, however,
that another observer put the population for the whole
Vale at 50,000, using the more normal contemporary
standard of three acres per cow unit; but to judge from the
fact that there were only 35,000 dairy cows in the whole
county nearly seventy years later, Marshall was probably
the more accurate.

Estimates of total cheese production vary likewise from
Marshall's 1,000 tons to Warner's 7,000-8,000. Marshall
explains his figures, Warner does not, so again Marshall's
estimate was probably the more accurate.

Milking was done on an 11 : 13 hour cycle, at 5 a.m. and
4 p.m., which gave the dairymaids plenty of daylight hours
to devote to their cheesemaking. Some of it was sold at
Gloucester market two or three times a year by its
producers, but by far the largest proportion was sold to
dealers known as 'cheese factors', who then resold it in
London, the Northern cities and abroad. Some of them
waxed fat from this business: two of them practically
divided up the entire produce of the Vale of Berkeley
between them. Berkeley had long been the centre of the
cheese industry — Double Gloucester was known as
'Double Berkeley' within the county — and the best
cheese was to be found within only a ten mile radius of the
village, notably at Hardwicke, Haresfield, Leonard
Stanley, Slimbridge, Stonehouse, Whitminster and at
Frocester, home of one of the two cheese tycoons and later
to become a great centre for experimental cheesemaking.

Marshall pointed out that 'it was the Gloucestershire
breed which raised the Gloucestershire dairy to its greatest

height', which led him to caution, with much justification and considerable foresight, against overuse of the Longhorn:

> 'the (Gloucester) breed has long been naturalised to the soil and situation; and certainly ought not to be supplanted, without some evident advantage, some clear gain, in the outset; nor even then, without mature deliberation; lest some unforeseen disadvantage should bring cause of repentance in the future'.

'We fear that Mr Marshall has here written incautiously', came the expected comment from the 'Monthly Review' critic, smugly confident with Bakewell's astounding success story keeping the agricultural journalists supplied with as much copy as they wanted. But the Gloucester breed had been bypassed by the likes of Bakewell, and there was only one breeder that Marshall had heard of who had ever attempted to improve the breed: Henry Long of Boddington.*

Boddington Manor Farm, of which Long was the hereditary tenant, at that time consisted of 'about 275 acres of good Meadow and Pasture Ground (including

---

\* This identification of Marshall's 'Long of Boddington' is based upon purely circumstantial evidence, and it is quite possible that I have presumed too much. Boddington Manor Farm, in the tenure of Henry Long, is first advertised for reletting in December 1780, and further advertisements appeared periodically until January 1782, when it appears to have been relet to James Buckle, who died there in 1818 — when the tenancy is taken up by another Henry Long, who might have been a relative.

The reference to 'election strife' would appear to relate to the death of the local MP W.B. Webster at Cleeve Hill a few miles away, for his majority in the 1776 election had been only 47 votes, which had caused trouble then. But if this is the right connection, it creates as many problems as it solves. Firstly, Long was not listed in the 1779

about six acres of fine orcharding), and about 115 acres of rich arable land', and was watered by both the Chelt and the village millstream. The pasture was luxuriant:

> '. . . the soil five or six feet deep. The herbage white clover and raygrass; the young shoots of the raygrass as sweet as sugar! Much sweeter than any I have before examined. These grounds (late Long's) are, it seems, very good ones for grazing; but are difficult to make cheese from'.

This, then, was the setting for Long's breeding experiment; but the only thing known about his breeding technique is that the end result was the cow Marshall referred to as 'one of the handsomest and most desirable dairy cows I have yet seen', and whose description I have used in presenting a 'breed standard' in the introduction. Her height was roughly equivalent to a Friesian cow of the same age, but she was about a foot longer in the back and narrower in the girth, which with the statement that she was

> 'a genuine, and a fair specimen, as to form; but not as to size; the cows of that celebrated breed were, in general, considerably larger'

may help to create a visual impression of Long's herd. Other features that Marshall noted were

---

Poll Book, which makes it difficult to see how he could have been involved in 'election strife' at all; secondly, Webster's death occurred the same week that the farm was first advertised; and finally it would not have been legally possible, even in those days, to 'drive' an important and prosperous farmer out of anywhere. This makes me think that Long was leaving the area anyway, but perhaps made himself locally unpopular at the time of the election, and the information then reached Marshall in the garbled form he gives it in.

'The eye full and bright, the ears remarkably large, the head fine and chap clean, the bosom deep; and the brisket broad, and projecting forward. The shoulder thin with the points snug. The thigh likewise thin, notwithstanding the great width at the nache. The bag large and hanging backward; being leathery and loose to the bearing. The teats of middle size; gives much milk, and *holds it long*.

The tail large, the hide thin, and the bone remarkably fine. The colour a 'dark brown'; marked with white along the back and about the udder; with the legs, chap, and head, of a full, glossy, dark chocolate colour. The horns a polished white; tipped with black'.

From the reference to 'the great width of the nache', it appears that Long had bred out the only serious deficiency then attributed to the Gloucester (apart from its lack of beefiness):

'In the selection of cows, it requires considerable judgement to fix on those which, from the width of their haunches, offer a fair probability of easy calving; this is said not to be the case with the Gloucester breed, which are often thin and narrow behind, and therefore more liable to difficulty and mischief on those occasions'.[17]

And this sums up all that is known or can be inferred about Long's breeding policies; Marshall gives no indication as to how he achieved this end-result. Long had many advantages — a large acreage of excellent grassland, centrally placed buildings, and not leastly, the pick of the breed at low prices; but the only hint to his material success is the fact that a twelve-stall cowshed was built just before he left in 1781,

'driven out of the vale by some election strife, (a curse in every county)'.

If I have found the right Long (see footnote), then he could well have moved a couple of parishes over to Sandhurst, where his brother lived, and the farm restored to a relative (perhaps his son) in 1818. But in the meantime the new tenant, James Buckle, restocked the farm with 'the mixed Hereford and Longhorn breeds, remarkably good milkers'. . . .[18] Incidentally, the farm at one time boasted possession of the Boddington Oak, one of the oldest trees in the country:

> 'Its circumference at the ground . . . is somewhat more than eighteen yards . . . and at its smallest dimensions, namely, from five to six feet high, it is thirty six feet . . . the stem is quite hollow, being near the ground, a perfect shell, forming a capacious cell-sized room, which at the floor measures, one way, more than sixteen feet in diameter . . . it is still perfectly alive and fruitful, having this year a fine crop of acorns upon it'.[19]

The Boddington Oak unfortunately did not long outlive its master, and was burnt to the ground in 1790.

In the absence of more detailed information, Long's achievement is no clearer than his aims; it might even have been he who established the breed's colour pattern irreversibly. The only positive things that can be said in conclusion are that he probably failed to re-establish the Gloucester only because his work was cut short; and that, if the reference to calving problems was not merely a figment of Rudge's imagination (he is the only source), then Long failed to eradicate the problem in the breed as a whole.

The last decade of the century saw the consolidation of the Longhorn's hold upon the county, although the old breed did not entirely disappear:

> 'Notwithstanding the introduction of several varieties, yet in some old dairies, the Gloucestershire breed of cows is still much valued; such, however, of late years, has been the love of novelty and experiment, that few "packs", or stocks are to be found in the county of a uniform composition, and fewer, perhaps, where the genuine old stock is preserved'.[21]

# The Nineteenth Century

The first half of the last century saw a dramatic decline in the popularity of the Longhorn. The old Longhorn was a good dairy cow of ancient repute and was already expanding before Bakewell, and it was of course dairy Longhorns that Marshall noticed swamping the Gloucestershire dairies; but as Bakewell's beef Longhorns became the fashion of the day, replacement stock for the Longhorn dairy herds came increasingly from cattle bred for beef, and this ruined the breed. Half a century later the Longhorn

> 'had acquired a delicacy of constitution, inconsistent with common management and keep; and it began, slowly but undeniably to deteriorate'.[21]

By 1846

> 'A very large part of the cattle of Britain consists of a mixture of races, having no uniformity of character, and generally defective in some important points'.[22]

— degenerate, miserable shadows of their 'purebred' ancestors, the breeding stock left behind when the beef bubble began to burst. Milk yields were actually decreasing in Gloucestershire. A sample of fifteen herds in Tortworth and Wickwar taken in 1834 found that the average lactation yield from about 3½ acres of keep was just under 4 cwt of cheese (roughly 400 lbs of milk), while thirty years later another survey found that much the same yield was needing nearly 5 acres of keep.[23] The dairy industry was consequently in a state of decay, Gloucestershire's once famous cheese was branded as 'inferior', and many Vale farmers were turning to beef:

> 'The fall in the value of Gloucestershire dairy produce is considerable; a cow which yielded cheese and butter worth about £9 last year, producing not more than £6 10s. 0d. this year for the farmers'.[24]

Having thus commercially ruined two formerly good dairy breeds, one (the Gloucester) through fashion, and the other (the Longhorn) through Bakewell's misguided attempts to beef it up, Gloucestershire farmers had to look elsewhere for their dairy stock. Apparently the Gloucester managed to rally briefly, perhaps following the Leonard Stanley and Kingscote Sales (see below); but if this was indeed the case it was doomed to failure by the remarkable rise of the Shorthorn.

Four major herds of Gloucesters are known to have existed until this time: the Badminton herd, of which more later, the Kingscote herd on the Cotswolds, and two in the Vale of Gloucester. Of these the largest was the herd of Samuel Brown (1792-1841) at Priory Farm, Leonard Stanley. Brown 'highly prided himself' on his 140 cow herd, very large for those days, which included 47 dairy cows and three bulls. The herd was dispersed in October 1842 and March 1843, when the Duke of Beaufort was amongst the buyers. Richard Hewlett (1762-1841) kept twenty five cows and two bulls at Church Farm, Frampton-on-Severn, and was renowned 'as a breeder of true Gloucestershire cattle' when his herd was dispersed in March 1842. Of the herd of Colonel Thomas Kingscote (1799-1861) I can discover nothing beyond the fact that it was sold in 1852, when the Duke of Beaufort, his brother-in-law, was again among the buyers. It is a pity that so little is known about these early enthusiasts, but as they witnessed one anothers' Wills it is probable that they were good friends, and that there was some interchange of stock between them; Lawson was probably writing about these breeders when in 1827 he referred to the Gloucester as being 'highly eligible dairy stock'.

But Shorthorns were the order of the day, following the astronomic success of the Colling brothers at Kirklevington in Yorkshire, who applied Bakewell's techniques to improving their local cattle breed, with considerably more lasting success. Sir Thomas Kingscote founded the first pedigree Shorthorn herd in the West Country in 1845 — a reason, perhaps, for his abandoning the Gloucester — and Earl Ducie of Tortworth Court, and Baron Fitzhardinge at Berkeley Castle, followed suit. Ducie's herd was dispersed in 1853, when the prices were 'without previous parallel', and Fitzhardinge's in 1868; and there can be little doubt that their success impressed and influenced their tenants and neighbours. Youatt observed in 1835 that the Shorthorn was already gaining ground, although the great majority were crossbreds:

'Each farmer breeds and chooses according to his pleasure or caprice . . . in all of them, however, traces of the old Gloucester are visible, and are carefully preserved'.

This last tradition, incidentally, was maintained until recent years, for many Vale farmers favoured using a Gloucester bull to produce a high-yielding heifer.

Any hopes of reviving the Gloucester as a nationally appreciated dairy cow were finally crushed by the decline in cheesemaking in the county. Milk had been sent to Bristol and Bath for many years, but it was not until the great London rinderpest epidemic of the mid-1860's, which killed about 80% of the city's cattle population, that 'railway milk' became a truly viable proposition when carried from as far away as Gloucestershire. There remained a place for other breeds of dairy cattle until that time, for if the quantity of their milk could not match the Shorthorn, the quality was that much better and thus suited to cheesemaking; but the new demand for liquid milk sounded the death knell for Gloucestershire's cheese industry.

Marshall had felt that cheese quality was declining as long ago as 1789, Youatt cast aspersions on the dairymaids' abilities in 1835, Caird was appalled by a Gloucester dairy in 1851, and by 1854 Bravender was condemning Gloucester cheese as 'inferior'. Always dwarfed by comparison with its southern neighbour (Cheddar), Double Gloucester manufacture had become almost a craft industry by the end of the century; and it was not, indeed, until after the last war that it began to be easily available again. Dr Francis Bond, of Gloucester, attributed the decline to the Gloucestershire farmer's reluctance to move with the times:

> 'It is of little use for him to make such cheese of the ancient type by which the reputation of Gloucestershire as a cheese county was first established . . . it is evident . . . that the county has already lost its claim to being the source of any special cheese which the public can recognise as such . . . Gloucestershire must adapt its cheesemaking as much as it can to make the cheeses which the public most wants . . . small and soft rather than large and firm'.[25]

Bond then called a three day 'National Cheese Conference' at Gloucester in 1884, which spawned both the celebrated Gloucester Dairy School, for many years financed out of his own pocket, and the Gloucester Dairy Association. It was indeed quite an achievement, and through his 'Severn Valley Dairy Produce Company' at

Stonehouse, Bond achieved considerable success with a variety of cheeses which were merely faintly disguised versions of the original. 'Little Gloucesters' were 'originally designed to meet the requirements of those who desire a palatable and digestible cheese', and even won the approval of Queen Victoria! 'Gloucester Roundels' followed later, but they were just circular versions of his square 'Little Gloucesters'; they were 'designed . . . for the purpose of encouraging a large consumption of cheese, a too-much neglected article of diet, and also for promoting the special Gloucestershire industry of cheesemaking'; and he also created a deconstipating Gloucester cheese called 'Casona', a 'purified' version. Dr Bond died in 1912, and his revamped Double Gloucester with him; he had a more lasting memorial in the Dairy School, for the World Wars 'hit Gloucester cheese harder than any other existing county variety'. During both world wars Double Gloucester suffered the further ignominy of being marketed as Cheddar!

But to return to the Gloucester cow, and to the greatest Gloucester herd of all time: Badminton.

There is not a shadow of doubt that, had it not been for the stalwart dedication of the Dukes of Beaufort to the breed, the Gloucester would have disappeared amid the outcrossings that followed the 'Longhorn invasion'. Whilst their latter-day claim to have actually created the breed by importing cattle from estates sequestrated during the Civil War can be dismissed as a pretty fiction, it is true that for a century and a half at least Badminton was a major fattening centre, buying in cattle from Wales as well as from Scotland and Devon. Occasionally cows and heifers were brought in along with the oxen, and their progeny no doubt contributed to the foundation stock of the herd. The first reference to the Gloucester breed as such in the Badminton records does not occur until 1805, and in 1807 a

A Badminton cow at the turn of the century. R. Wallace, *Farm Live Stock of Great Britain*, 2nd ed. 1907

Gloucester bull was bought from one Richard Hook for £26 6s. 0d., but both Earl Bathurst and Morgan Evans estimated that the herd was founded in the 1780s, which seems a reasonable date. A Berkeley Estate account book of 1771 refers to 'the best dairy cows sent to Badminton', the earliest reference I have discovered to a dairy herd there. 'A Load of Chees' was sold from Badminton in 1772, and cheese was sold at Tetbury in the early nineteenth century — but as the Duke was also building up a Channel Island herd at that time it is quite possible that this cheese came from them and not from Gloucesters. There is a reference to 'knobling of 48 cows horns' in 1775-76 — presumably indicating a 24 cow herd — and admittedly this was a local tradition; but it had become a distinguishing characteristic of the herd by the 1890's, and there could be some link. It certainly implies at least that there was a small herd of cows already distinct from the scores of beef cattle passing through the estate at that time. We shall probably never know exactly when the Dukes first decided to establish a purebred Gloucester herd, but it was already well-known by 1842, and from 1846 the estate accounts are full of references to old Gloucester cows being sold fat.

The Badminton herd in the late nineteenth century was managed more or less in the manner which Marshall had described as being general Vale practice a century earlier. Cows were calved during the winter months, and the calves left on their dams for ten days before being weaned off rapidly on skimmed milk; the heifers were served at about two years old, coming into milk during their third winter. They were kept outdoors all the year round, and merely yarded in the winter, but they held a steady daily yield of about 2½-3½ gallons for a long time; and as the Gloucester lactation was much more regular than, for instance, the Friesian, the yield over a 305 day lactation might thus have been as much as 900 gallons. This was a tribute to the good breeding policies and sound management of the Beaufort family and of their managers, for the average national yield after the turn of the century was estimated at 531 gallons.

Apart from a small injection of Glamorgan blood in 1884-85, when cattle were bought from the eccentric Dr Price of Llantrissant (see p.82) to remedy a 50% infertility rate in the heifers, no outside blood was introduced into the herd between 1852 and 1919. Numbers were kept up to about 100 head, half of which were milkers, and all draught cows were culled at about eight years. Although these cattle weighed about 800-1,000 lbs, (comparable with today's Guernsey or Dairy Shorthorn), they had

'a larger portion of lean meat to fat than most animals, and are considered by the butchers "good cutters"; but I have no doubt a well-bred Shorthorn would make 3 lbs of meat from the same food that a Gloucester would require to make 2 lbs.'[26]

Owing to the letting of one of the Badminton estate's home farms, thirty cows and fifteen steers were sold at an auction on October 14 1896, the first major sale of Gloucesters for forty four years. That sale could have made or broken the breed, for if the cattle had gone to the dealers the breed would probably have petered out over the next few decades, with Badminton as its graveyard. As it was, however, interest was considerable, and several new herds were established as a result of it. The thirty cows were sold for £544, and the steers for £193; amongst the buyers were Sir Lionel Darell and Granville Lloyd-Baker, the two breeders whose herds were ultimately to form the nucleus of the Gloucestershire Cattle Society.

The Darell family moved to Fretherne Court, Saul, from Yorkshire in the early nineteenth century, and Sir

Lionel (1845-1919) built up a herd of about thirty milkers and seventy followers on the estate's 100 acre Barrow Hill farm. His cattle were apparently larger and beefier than the Gloucester is today, and it has been suggested that Darell built up a beef herd of Gloucester cattle. The few people old enough to remember the herd recollect the use of brass horn-knobs, (thus continuing the practice at Badminton), that Darell's cattle had much less white than today's, and that tenants on the Fretherne estate took their cows to his bulls for service, which resulted in Gloucester breeding being very evident in the area long after the herd was dispersed. Darell was badly hit financially by the war, and in 1917 had to begin the winding-up of the estate. The Gloucester herd was sold in March 1919, and prices reached £58.

Probably the only herd apart from Badminton to survive the nineteenth century was that of Christopher Carter, of Gravel Court Farm, Brookthorpe. Carter was deemed to be an authority on the breed, and his comments on breed characteristics no doubt influenced the Society when they were deciding on the 'Points of the Breed' in 1919. This is all that is known of the herd, except that Lloyd-Baker's herd at Hardwicke was founded on 'a beautiful cow from the famous old herd at Gravel Court Farm'. Granville Lloyd-Baker (1846-1924) built up an important herd on the 1,700 acre home farm at Hardwicke Court; but again I can trace very little about it, beyond the fact that the herd appears to have been dispersed at much the same time as Sir Lionel Darell's herd; oddly there are no cattle credited to his breeding in the herd book, which however teems with Fretherne cows. Lloyd-Baker's interest survived his herd, and he was not only one of the prime motivators behind the establishment of the Society in 1919, but acted also as its Honorary Secretary until his death in 1924. Sir John Dorington (1832-1911) of Lypiatt Park, Stroud, and one-time president of the Gloucester Dairy Association, is mentioned as having a herd in 1907, which was probably based on stock purchased at Badminton in 1896 and in view of the connection with Dr Bond, might possibly have been producing cheese; and Sir Gerald Codrington (1850-1929), whose family had lived at Dodington House, Tormarton (near Badminton) for centuries, kept a small herd of Gloucesters at a secondary manor house there. Codrington also bred Jerseys and Shorthorns until 1900, but his Gloucester herd lingered into Society days. It was largely dispersed at Yate in 1925.

Publicity for the breed increased noticeably in the years following the Badminton sale. Wallace prepared the first illustrated article on the breed in 1907, and a year later the Badminton herd featured in a magnificently illustrated article in 'Country Life'. The Duke, no doubt encouraged by this new wave of interest in the breed, took some Gloucesters along to the 1909 Royal Show at Gloucester:

'Great interest was aroused at the Gloucester Royal by a group of this breed, which were, however, not for competition . . . the cow showed many points which indicate deep milking qualities. Her quarters were well-shaped and long, the skin fine and mellow, the tail long and well carried, the chine beautifully formed and fine, and the rib well sprung and deep. The back showed very typically the wedge shape so much admired by the milch cow enthusiast . . . it cannot be said that (the bull) showed so much quality as the cows. He was, nevertheless, a strong robust-looking beast . . . it was remarked by several from amongst the great numbers who inspected these cattle at the show, that the breed was very 'Welsh' in type . . . it might even be truthfully said that . . . (the cow) showed points both of limb and body which would please the Jersey man . . . the cattlemen in charge were enthusiastic in praise of their stock, and told us that animals of this breed were seldom, if ever, under a roof and that notwithstanding this a cow sixteen years old, which in her prime had given

o Badminton cows, *Broad* and *Charmer*. W. Roach, *Country Life, 1908.*

6½ gallons of good quality milk, made £21 to the butcher when fat'.[27]

The Show succeeded in getting the breed official recognition, for it was given an entry in the Ministry of Agriculture's 'British Breeds of Livestock' a year later. Interest aroused by the display was such that plans were made then and there to form a breed society, but, probably through lack of sufficient herds, the idea was postponed until after the sales at Fretherne and Hardwicke in 1919, which spawned a whole new generation of enthusiastic Gloucester breeders.

*Dymock Primrose*

# Interest at Last:
## The First Gloucester Cattle Society

The Gloucester was one of the last cattle breeds to acquire a breed society and herdbook, a century after the Shorthorn; the surprising thing is that it acquired one at all, after a century of decline, decay and ultimate near-extinction. Interest in creating a society was undoubtedly triggered off by the Fretherne sale a few months earlier, and it was formed largely on the initiative of three men: Granville Lloyd-Baker of Hardwicke Court, Stanley Williams of New Park, Falfield, and Colonel Elwes of Colesbourne Park, Cheltenham. Together with half a dozen devotees of the breed, they met at the Bell Hotel, Gloucester, on June 19th 1919:

> 'Mr Granville Lloyd-Baker presided, and said he was very interested in the breeding of old Gloucester cattle. He advocated their use not only for the sake of the old county breed, but because he knew them to be very valuable, particularly in regard to the making of cheese . . . the Duke of Beaufort was elected president for a year, the Chairman remarking that it was thanks to the Duke's family that the breed had been preserved. The Duke's herd was the oldest in the county, and had been kept going through all changes of fashion . . . the Chairman said the idea in forming the Society was to encourage as many registered herds of Old Gloucester cattle as possible. With the formation of the Society, breeders would know where to apply in order to get pedigree stock'.[28.]

On August 7th, a Committee met to establish the points of the breed, working from which they were able to locate and register 130 animals in 14 herds by February 1920, and several more were discovered by 1922; these constituted the foundation stock of the breed. Initially there was a very wide membership, for the most part small herds in the Vale of Gloucester, but including members from as far afield as Suffolk and London; by 1925 the Society had registered over 300 cattle, in 25 herds.

The question of selective outcrossing to improve the genetic stock and the commercial performance of the breed was tackled from the outset, but preliminary tests on milk quality were so good that it was not until 1925 that the Society finally agreed to sanction an official upgrading programme, and then only from first-cross Welsh Black, Shorthorn or Lincoln Red cows. In the event very few breeders actually did outcross, the most notable being Earl Bathurst at Cirencester (page 55 ).

Showing was another aspect of cattle breeding that was fostered early on by the Society, which realised the need for publicity. In 1920 two classes were booked at both the Bath and West of England at Salisbury and at the smaller Berkeley Hunt show in the breed's heartland. In 1922 the Bath and West classes were replaced by the newly-formed Three Counties Show, that year held at Gloucester; the old Lemon and Parker Inn at Gloucester presented the Society with its first challenge trophy. The breed continued to show at the Three Counties until 1938; the decline in cattle numbers and the introduction of classes for tuberculin-tested cattle only after the war put the breed out of the commercial showring for thirty-six years. The Gloucester managed to produce fourteen entrants from five herds for the three classes allocated for the breed at the 1936 Bristol Royal Show however; and ten years later two Colesbourne cows were on show as a curiosity at the

Bath and West of England Farm Week, again at Bristol.

The first few years of the Society were halcyon days for the breed; interest in the infant Society came from as far away as Canada and Salt Lake City, and a search instigated by the Society in 1926 succeeded in locating one survivor of the Glamorgan breed, which was duly registered as 'Glamorgan Breed Foundation Stock'. Two major dispersal sales took place in the early twenties, which disseminated several valuable bloodlines throughout the breed, for although both herds were based on Badminton stock they had been developing separately for decades.

F.A. Davies' 28-cow herd was established at Scots Farm, Pinckney, Wiltshire, at the turn of the century; and although Davies was never a member of the Society, the dispersal sale which followed his death in December 1920 was well attended by Society members, who paid record prices for the cattle; the average price was nearly £70, the top price 152 guineas — a tribute to the Society's success in renewing interest in the breed.

The other major sale was that of A.T. Bentley, of Woodlands House, Southampton. His herd of 14 cows was developed from a Gloucester herd in the New Forest belonging to the Hon. Edward Powell, of Little Testwood, Totton, in turn based on Badminton blood. Bentley's herd was sold at Badminton on May 3 1921, when the average price was £56.

Both these herds had represented potential spearheads into 'foreign' country, and possibly the reconcentration of cattle back into Gloucestershire was unfortunate for the breed; certainly the principal buyers were those who were later to become the nucleus of stalwarts who persevered with the breed until after the Second War, so perhaps the diffusion of blood was not so great as it might have been.

Because of the breed's ancient reputation as a cheese producer, the Society concentrated on developing the dairy aspects first and foremost:

> 'too much stress cannot be laid on the fact that the milking ability of the breed must be regarded as a factor for future development'.[29]

An early analysis of Gloucester milk revealed an average butterfat of 4.67%, and a solids-not-fat of 8.205%; following this the Society urged its members to milk-record their cattle and to obtain butterfat percentages. Several breeders then proceeded to do so, and the average for all milk records in the herdbook — 7,419 lbs in 360 days — is astonishingly high, considering that the then national average was about 550 gallons, and that the Gloucester had been neglected as a commercial animal for so long. The butterfat percentage regularly reached 6%, and in 1935 the Society felt justified in lobbying the MMB for a 1d per gallon 'Gold Top' premium for Gloucester milk. They did not succeed; perhaps if they had, the breed would be more common today. As interest in the breed declined, however, only two breeders really devoted much time to improving milk yields — Colonel Elwes and Earl Bathurst. Lt-Colonel Henry Cecil Elwes (1874-1950) of Colesbourne Park was without a doubt the staunchest devotee of the breed, right up until his death in 1950. His herd was founded on a bull and seven cows bought at the Fretherne sale and averaged about 700 gallons '700 feet up in the Cotswolds', on grass and home-produced cereals alone. His first high-yielding cow was bred at Pinckney — *Ladyswood Pansy 190*; she gave 7,132 lbs in her third lactation, 8,314 lbs in her fourth and 9,214 in her fifth. A Woodlands cow, *Colesbourne Bluebell 54*, gave 6,000 lbs in her first lactation, 8,712 lbs in her second and 9,102 lbs in her third at 5% butterfat and 8.45% solids-not-fat, i.e. a total solids of 14.25%; she also won the first Lemon and Parker Cup at the 1923 Three

Counties Show, and played a major part in establishing Earl Bathurst's Ciceter herd. Seymour Henry, 7th Earl Bathurst, joined the Society in 1922 and purchased a few heifers and a young bull in the same year. He rapidly rose to prominence within the breed society, remodelling the herdbook on more practical lines in 1924 and augmenting breed publicity by writing articles on it; he also went to considerable lengths to locate finchback breeds around the world. He

> 'had an idea that it woud be a good thing to introduce some outside blood, as for many years the purebred Gloucester must have been terribly inbred',

and early on established a policy of 'careful outcrossing' to Shorthorn cows, 'quietly working to grade up Gloucester cattle to the coveted 1,000 gallon cow'; in this he succeeded with the halfbred cow *Ciceter Rubra A17,* who reached 11,013 lbs in the fourth lactation. Her dam was a Shorthorn, her sire *Badminton Starlight 238*, a bull used extensively by Bathurst in his upgrading programme. Descended from Fretherne and Woodlands stock, *Starlight* was sold to Bathurst by the Duke of Beaufort in August 1922, and came first at the Three Counties in 1922 and 1923. The Ciceter herd was built on as wide a spectrum of the breed as possible, by 1926 containing 6 bulls and 31 cows from ten different herds, but Bathurst was still unsatisfied with the performance of his herd, and decided to improve it by introducing White Park blood, a breed which he somehow deduced to be of Welsh origin and therefore a likely ancestor of the Gloucester. Bathurst borrowed a White Park bull from Lord Dynevor, and embarked upon an upgrading scheme as interesting as it was futile. Of seven calves from Gloucester cows, two had almost perfect Gloucester markings, four were black with the Gloucester finchback, and the other two had White

*Cicester Howsthat 309*, photographed in 1927; one of the first generation of Gloucesters to be bred at Cirencester. *Museum of English Rural Life, Reading.*

*Badminton Starlight 238*, a bull extensively used by Earl Bathurst to upgrade high-yielding shorthorns. *Gloucester Cattle Society.*

Park markings; five calves from halfbred cows had colours ranging from light dun to black, only one retaining Gloucester markings. This experiment was not repeated, as Bathurst lost the 'satiny coat' which endeared the breed to his parkland panorama, but the urge to experiment died hard, and the Earl persevered with his outcrossing until his death in 1943. Always interested in agriculture, Bathurst at one time had the only team of oxen in the county — which was remembered by his executors, who arranged for his coffin to be carried on a farm wagon drawn by an ox!

Other breeders of those early years included Stanley Williams of New Park, Falfield, whose nineteen cow herd was based largely on Fretherne stock (it was dispersed in January 1923); and Martin Gazzard of Sanigar, Sharpness (later of World's End Farm, Berkeley). Gazzard was one of the pioneers of the Society, and contributed many suggestions for its improvement; his small herd was again founded on Pinckney and Woodlands blood, and was dispersed in 1926.

Of more durable importance to the breed were the Ladies Susan (1878-1965) and Victoria (1879-1963) Hicks-Beach, daughters of the famous Victorian statesman Sir Michael Hicks-Beach; they maintained a small but select herd of Gloucesters on their Williamstrip Park estate at Coln St Aldwyn's, on the Cotswolds, for much of the Society's existance.

Major Sir Frederick Cripps, of Ampney Park, Cirencester (1873-1959), maintained a home farm Gloucester herd of about ten cows until 1950, selling milk locally from his better-known Shorthorn herd, and exchanged cattle regularly with his son-in-law Robert, 5th Baron Cromwell, of Misterton Hall, Lutterworth, Warwickshire. It was Cromwell who purchased the Glamorgan cow referred to earlier, and he built up a fine Gloucester herd which was dispersed in 1939; his bull *Misterton Colour Seargent 631* became Earl Bathurst's stock bull, and sired over a quarter of the cattle listed in the 1945 herdbook.

It was with justification that 'Middlehorn', in the 'Farmer and Stockbreeder Yearbook' for 1923, could say that

> 'The Gloucestershire Cattle Society has every reason to feel satisfied with the progress that has been made during the last four years, and there can be no doubt that it has been working on the right lines',

but the momentum soon withered under the burden of a threefold catastrophe of an impact that was barely realised at the time. Foot-and-mouth disease swept across Gloucestershire and one of the earliest victims was the seven-cow herd of Thomas Webb at Hardwicke. This herd was probably based on Badminton stock, as Webb's father had once farmed at Badminton, no doubt augmented by cattle from the herd of his landlord, Granville Lloyd-Baker; Webb had just increased his numbers to twelve when the disease struck, and the Ministry of Agriculture's compulsory slaughter policy finished the job. The Gloucester's white finchback acquired a gruesome advantage here, for it allowed the Ministry slaughtermen to work well into the night! The Society sympathised:

> 'Whilst in ordinary circumstances, the loss of cattle is an exceedingly serious item, in the case of a breed in the position the Gloucestershires are, the slaughter of Mr Webb's herd is little short of a calamity for the Society in the depressing influence it has upon the general success of the breed . . .' and in 'trusting that despite the great setback he has received, he will do all in his power to further the objects for which this Society was formed'.[30]

They were being hopelessly optimistic. Webb remained a member until 1926, but he never registered any more cattle; and all the indications are that the epidemic virtually annihilated the rank-and-file breeders, who presumably restocked with Shorthorns.

Then the death of Granville Lloyd-Baker deprived the breed of a most knowledgeable, experienced and dedicated Secretary, and though his successor Lionel Harrisson, of Mathon Court, Worcestershire, was able and generous, taking cuts in his small salary in times of financial crisis, he never gained the prestige and influence of his predecessor, despite his twenty-year service to the breed, because he lacked Lloyd-Baker's personal involvement with it and was too distant from the main body of the breeders to become better-known.

The other catastrophe for the breed was the death of the Duke of Beaufort, whose family connection with it was matched by a keen interest of his own — an enthusiastic figurehead. The herd was maintained by his successor, the tenth Duke, but he lacked the enthusiasm or the ability of his forebears, and the herd, already suffering from inbreeding despite the introduction of two bulls from Fretherne (*Badminton Jock 1*) and Woodlands (*Badminton Bentley 2*), went into a sharp decline. By the 1930's the Duke had to introduce Shorthorn blood in order to maintain the herd at all, and not even considerable use of Ciceter blood (itself of doubtful purity) could prevent the herd of the 1940's from being a pale shadow of its predecessor.

The effect of the triple disaster was to reduce the Society to a core of dedicated members. Registrations tailed off dramatically due to the epidemic, but they failed to rally as dramatically after it, the 1927 figure of 177 cattle in 13 herds being the post-epidemic peak; this was followed by a rapid decline, which gathered momentum as the Depression began to bite.

'From about 1924 or 1925 the Society was simply a plaything

for half a dozen gentry inspired by tradition rather than economics',

was William Bathurst's epitaph on the breed in 1966, and it is a statement amply borne out by the Society membership, and the fact that by 1930 only two out of nine herds, and 16 out of 142 cattle were not owned by members with pedigrees considerably longer than that of their cattle. This is not to condemn their efforts however; had it not been for the county aristocracy the breed would certainly have petered out by the 1930's, and all of the herds paid their way. Like their eighteenth century forebears, the rural nobility of the 1930's were able to devote time and money to improving the breed, as the examples of Colonel Elwes and Earl Bathurst bear witness. But this time the big estates themselves were not invulnerable, starved of labour by the social upheaval that followed the Great War, and literally 'landed' with unlettable farms. Many of today's most prosperous farmers were able to acquire their farms for peanuts in the thirties and forties. One by one the landed gentry were forced to give up their commercial Gloucester herds, and by 1935 only six functional members were left in the Society.

With the Second World War came the ploughing-up of much of Gloucestershire's ancient permanent pasture, and these few remaining breeders were forced to run down their herds; but even their enthusiasm was beginning to wane because of the Society's loss of vitality. The Society hoped to survive the War because of the suspension of showing and the consequent expense; and luckily for the breed it rejected a startling proposal by the Duke of Beaufort that all calf registration should be suspended during the War, for it hoped that the high prices and demand for pedigree cattle which had brought the Society into existence after the First World War would be repeated after the Second. It was not until 1942, however, that the

*ninton Perfect II 175*, one of the best known Gloucesters of the 1920's. *Museum*
*nglish Rural Life, Reading.*

*bourne.* Colonel Elwes with an unknown heifer of his breeding. Considering
important the Colesbourne herd to the genetic make-up of the breed today,
regretable that there are so few photographs that can be reliably accredited to
herd. *H.W.G. Elwes.*

Society admitted its plight and resolved to cajole Eric Dowdeswell of Wick Court, Saul, into joining the Society.

The Wick Court herd was founded by Robert Dowdeswell from two first-cross heifers of unknown origin; but as the 148-acre farm was part of Sir Lionel Darell's estate until 1919, it is probable that Dowdeswell's interest, if not his herd, dates from the Fretherne Sale. Dowdeswell joined the Society in June 1923, and during the 1920's the herd was gradually built up to about ten cattle, the names characterised by the initial letter 'M'. The first bull used at Wick Court was of Badminton breeding — *Bentley's Smart I 244*, and together with a Cirencester bull bought in 1935, and a Coln bull bought in 1946, constituted the only recorded introduction of outside blood until the late 1960's. Robert Dowdeswell died in April 1929, and the herd passed to his son Eric Dowdeswell who continued to build it up, but did not continue his father's membership of the Society. In 1942, therefore, the Society made its first tentative attempts to woo back the Dowdeswell family. It took them two years of diplomacy, and as the herd had lost its pedigree status they had to drastically revise the Society's existing constitution in order to accommodate the herd. From 1922 non-pedigree cattle could only be registered in the supplementary herdbook, and had to be registered by an inspection committee of four; but as there were only half a dozen ageing members left, the rules had to be rewritten to suit them. The Council was cut from seven members to three, the inspection committee from four members to two, the Council no longer undertook to inspect each herd every year — and the ruling on pedigree stock was removed. The twenty four animals at Wick Court were thus brought back into the fold in March 1944, and were registered *en masse* at half price. Presumably unbeknown to the Society there were other small herds of Gloucesters still extant, at Dursley, and at Elmore, Cam and Nympsfield in the Vale of Berkeley; no doubt the loss of these bloodlines had its effect upon the Gloucester 'gene bank'.

The Badminton stock bull, in the early days of the Society, was *Badminton Bentley 2*, a bull used so extensively and to such effect that he can justly be called 'the Father of the Breed' as it stands today. This bull was bred by A.F. Bentley at Woodlands in Hampshire (page 53), and was exchanged as a calf for a Badminton animal. Amongst his sons were *Badminton Bentley's Smart I 244*, Dowdeswell's first stock bull, and *Badminton Starlight 238*, mentioned earlier as being the bull used by Earl Bathurst in his upgrading programme. Three of his daughters averaged 7,617 lbs in 351 days in their first lactations, a remarkable achievement considering the inbreeding at Badminton; and one of them, *Badminton Perfect II 175*, received more contemporary acclaim than any Gloucester until Eric Freeman's *Bemborough Saul 848* in the 1970's. She gave 7,700 lbs in her first lactation, and through her six daughters spread these dairy characteristics throughout the herd. But the old bull was used far too heavily at Badminton — he sired no less than 42 animals within the one herd — and the Badminton genetic pool was far too limited to support such Bakewellian 'in-and-in' breeding techniques for long. Fertility problems in the next few years decimated the herd, and only one cow of true Badminton stock was left in 1942! For months the Duke searched around for replacement stock, and he finally induced Earl Bathurst to sell him a bull (*Ciceter Czar 235*) and a few heifers, themselves of dubious ancestry. From June 1944 the herd was registered in the Duchess's name; she took a keen interest in the herd, even doing the milking during the war. She tried valiantly to rebuild the herd, but the new blood had arrived too late. By 1950 all the milkers had died or had been crossed out,

and the last few Gloucester heifers at Badminton were fattened for slaughter the same winter, an ignominious end to such a herd.

Colonel Elwes at Colesbourne had by now become convinced that the decline of the Gloucester was due to fall off in demand for Gloucester cheese:

'If there is a revival of cheesemaking and dual-purpose cattle again come into their own, there ought to be a demand again for Gloucester cattle'.[31]

Elwes practiced what he preached, making cheese at Colesbourne from 1942:

'The superiority of cheese made from Gloucester milk will be acknowledged by any who have had the opportunity to make the comparison'.[32]

Elwes' activities attracted the notice of Vincent Yorke, of Forthampton Court near Tewkesbury, who made Double Gloucester cheese on his home farm; he bought a bull and five heifers from Colesbourne, which became the nucleus of a herd which lasted into the early fifties.

Another man to have a brief flirtation with the Gloucester was Sir Claud Alexander, a breeder of White Park cattle from Faygate in Sussex. Alexander's interest in the Gloucester dated from the time when he acquired one of Earl Bathurst's experimental crossbred heifers (page 55), a daughter of which, by a White Park bull, gave 11,724 lbs in her first lactation; and until his death in 1946 Alexander ran a small herd of Gloucesters alongside his White Parks.

Earl Bathurst died in September 1943, and the herd was taken over by his youngest son, Ralph Bathurst (1905-1965). Dedicated to the breed, Bathurst was young and ambitious and he found the Society lethargic and moribund: 'I will have nothing to do with breeders who are making a mess of the breed', he declared — and walked out on the 1943 A.G.M., an embarrassment for the Society, which was holding the meeting, as for many years past, in the Cirencester estate office. A proposal for the setting-up of a milk recording scheme was added to the Society Constitution in an effort to appease him — and in the meantime the Society held its meetings in a Gloucester cafe!

The Society, however, was rapidly becoming synonymous with Colonel Elwes; when Harrisson resigned as Secretary in 1946, Elwes' son-in-law George Dusgate took over, and the offices were transferred to Colesbourne; the publication of the sixth — and final — herd book a year earlier was only made possible through a donation from his wife.

The Society had belatedly joined the National Cattle Breeder's Association in 1945, and Elwes contributed an article on the breed, and his herd in particular, to their publication 'British Pedigree Cattle' in 1947. Dusgate's appointment as Secretary was confirmed for June 1947, but his duties were light: no cattle had been shown in competition anywhere for a decade, and registrations were halving annually. Elwes did succeed in inducing Ralph Bathurst to join the Society, in December 1946.

Bathurst's animated approach was in stark contrast to that of the stagnant Society:

'We believe that Gloucesters are just a little better than the best . . . we believe that they will stand up to the finest dairy cattle in the country. We have made our plans, but in the meantime we can only assure you that the Gloucesters are coming back',

he announced to the farming world in 1946,[33] and he began to collect material for a 'breed census', but it was far too late to reverse the decline. The Hicks-Beach sisters moved to Wiltshire in 1946, leaving all but three of their Gloucesters to their nephew Earl St Aldwyn, who was not particularly interested. The Duchess resigned in December 1949 and Sir Frederick Cripps in July 1950, but the Society really ceased to exist on the death of Colonel Elwes in January 1950. A final Society meeting was held soon afterwards, which drew up some emergency measures — all members were to sit on the Council, and the inspection of cattle could be done 'by any expert' — but there was nobody left interested enough to continue the Society. The bulk of the Colesbourne herd was then sold to Bathurst in 1951, and a year later Earl St Aldwyn and Dusgate handed over the remains of the Society to him. Bathurst then estimated that there were about fifty cattle left, of which only those in his own herd and at Wick Court were to survive. For a while Bathurst maintained the pedigrees of his 'Ciren' herd; but any pedigrees later than 1952 are now lost, if indeed they ever existed, and as Dowdeswell never registered his cattle after 1949 the Society merged completely into the person of Ralph Bathurst. A phantom Society continued to be affiliated to the National Cattle Breeders' Association until Bathurst's death in 1965, and its deposit account had by 1966 reached £52 16s. 9d. This sum was claimed — and made over — to Eric Dowdeswell, and was finally given to the Church.

The first Gloucester Cattle Society was established on a wide membership, and was initially full of energy and ambition; yet within twenty years it had degenerated into the 'plaything of half a dozen landed gentry'. Not because of any economic fault — on the contrary the milk tests and yields of the 1920's were highly promising; but perhaps the Society became too cliquey too early and not enough effort was put into attracting the smaller farmers, who were quite possibly deterred from joining by the exalted membership of the Society. There is nothing in the records to indicate that it made any serious attempt to win back the small Gloucester breeders who left the Society in droves after the foot-and-mouth epidemic. Perhaps if it had been founded thirty years earlier, or later, the Society might have fared better; as it was, it was the victim of a series of calamities which crippled it in its infancy, and left the Society with a loss of direction and purpose that was never fully regained.

# THE GLOUCESTERSHIRE CATTLE SOCIETY

----

### President :

THE DUKE OF BEAUFORT, K.G.

### Council :

LIEUT.-COL. H. C. ELWES, M.V.O., D.S.O.
THE LADY SUSAN HICKS-BEACH.
SIR FREDERICK CRIPPS, BT.
MR. R. DOWDESWELL.

### Inspection Sub-Committee :

LIEUT.-COL. H. C. ELWES, M.V.O., D.S.O.
THE LADY SUSAN HICKS-BEACH.

### Secretary and Treasurer :

L. G. E. HARRISSON, Mathon Court, Malvern.

### Auditor :

L. H. C. BATT, Barclays Bank Limited, Malvern.

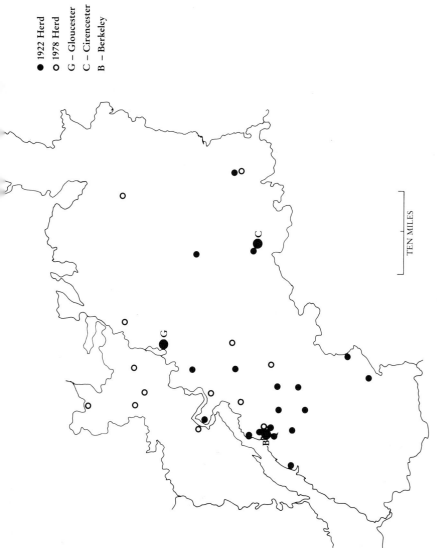

TEN MILES

The Gloucester at home: Gloucester herds in Gloucestershire, 1922 and 1978 based on the herdbooks.

# Renaissance

Twenty years of written silence followed the demise of the Society; and for much of the ensuing information I am thus indebted to a number of people's memories, but I cannot vouch for their accuracy!

Ralph Bathurst had an ear for rhetoric:

> 'Milk is my first object. I want cows with fine dairy heads, long necks, good udders, deep middles and plenty of room behind. Let them have black tongues, shiny coats, pretty hooves and flashing white tails, but above all that let them have udders with well-spaced teats . . . this is my idea of the Gloucester cow of the future, and it is a cow that will be popular all over the country. It can be done and I intend to do it, though we have some way to go.
>
> But what is the fun of breeding a lot of heavy-handed beasts with bushy tails, roman noses and large hairy ears? Are the cows to have no bags at all?'[34]

With this ambitious statement as his blueprint, Bathurst proceeded to build up a 170-cow herd at Elm Bank Farm, Cold Aston, on the top of the Cotswolds, from the remnants of his 'Ciren' herd, transferred from Cirencester in 1954 to make way for a Red Poll herd. He succeeded in boosting the milk yield, and the average yield of the cows dispersed in 1966 was 11,058 lbs at 3.56% butterfat; one of his cows — *Eva 10* — yielded the current Gloucester record of 16,785 lbs, at 3.56% butterfat. But he failed in his other goals, for he not only shunned publicity but, of more fundamental significance for the breed, he embarked upon a programme of outcrossing so extensive that ultimately the proportion of true Gloucester blood in the herd must have been small. Untramelled by Society dogma restricting the use of non-Gloucester animals, Bathurst soon introduced Friesian cows; and a 'Black Gloucester' bull was reared. A decade later there were only a handful of brown cattle in the herd, and from this stems a myth only now being dispelled — that Gloucesters of old were either brown or black according to the breeder's fancy. In later years Ayrshire, Red Poll and finally Friesian A.I. bulls were used; and the resultant pot-pourri was virtually a new breed in its own right.

There is no doubt at all that Bathurst was dedicated to his Gloucesters however, and despite his questionable breeding policies, his management was impeccable. Contract milking was used in later years, which may partially have accounted for the high yields; and 2½ lbs of concentrate per gallon was fed for production, maintenance coming from silage, kale and hay. Bathurst's Gloucesters became at last his sole interest; he knew every cow in the herd and visited the cattle daily from his home at Cirencester, despite increasingly bad attacks of Parkinson's disease, which drove him finally to suicide in December 1965.

Following his death, thirty of the best cattle were bought by the manager, and sent to Dorset, where their mongrelised descendants are still to be seen today; but of the 148 cattle sold on 6 September 1966, only about a dozen lived to be registered with the reborn Gloucester Cattle Society. Well over half went for slaughter, and a large batch sent to Cheshire were wiped out in the 1967 foot-and-mouth epidemic. A young bull called *Brewer* was bought by Major A.E. Savage of Sussex to assist in the rebuilding of a herd his family had had many years before, and he still has a small herd today; but the remainder of Bathurst's Gloucesters were scattered around the country and crossed out of existance.

The herd at Wick Court developed in almost complete isolation from Bathurst's, the only known exchange of blood being a few cows of the '*Fussy*' family, sent to the Dowdeswells by Bathurst in the late 1950's. Also a dairy herd, for over fifty years Wick Court sent milk to Cadbury's Dairy at Frampton-on-Severn, and no doubt the use of Gloucester milk contributed to the success of Cadbury's milk chocolate! The herd was built up to about fifty cattle, and a young stock bull was usually kept. From 1958 occasional surplus bulls were sold to Mr Peter King of Kite's Nest Farm, Whiteshill, whose suckler herd of Gloucesters is today registered with the Society with the prefix '*Shermanswood*'; and one of a very few others to purchase stock from Wick Court before the 1973 Sale was Mr Joe Henson, of Bemborough Farm, Guiting Power, on top of the Cotswolds. Henson it was who pioneered the 'farm park mania' of the 1970's, setting aside 25 of the 1,000 acres he farms in partnership with Mr John Neave for the Cotswold Farm Park. Henson's first cattle there were two Gloucesters from Wick Court: one proved to be barren, and the other (*Wick Court Ella 836*) 'was a super cow . . . but if you tried to milk her she'd kick you out of the shed!'

Eric Dowdeswell died in April 1968, and the herd passed to his sisters Ella and Alex Dowdeswell. The following year, on the suggestion of Mr Willie Young, the Ministry of Agriculture's Regional Livestock Officer, semen was taken from the young bull *Wick Court Gloucester* to save the breed from extinction. This remarkable piece of foresight is typical of Mr Young, who has ever been generous in giving the breed Society the benefit of his wide knowledge and experience.

Following an accident to one of the Miss Dowdeswells, the Wick Court herd had to be dispersed; and the sale, held on October 25 1972, ushered in a new and healthier era for the Gloucester. Enthusiasts such as Joe Henson and Eric Freeman of Newent, amongst others, paid high prices to save the breed from the dealers — the thirty three cattle sold averaged £200. One would-be purchaser missed the sale by a day: Charles Martell of Laurel Farm, Dymock, whose interest in the breed dates back to his childhood.

> 'Immediately after the Sale I contacted all the purchasers to see what their cattle were like, and I found that everybody had ones, or twos; the whole thing had to be co-ordinated before the breed became extinct'.

A meeting was then arranged at Whitminster House in May 1973, when forty-five people interested in saving the breed were brought together after months of preparation to reform the Gloucester Cattle Society. A Council was formed, with the initial task of locating, registering and inspecting the surviving animals, using as a blueprint for selection the 'Points of the Breed' as drawn up in 1919. Seventy of the best animals were registered as Foundation Stock; these form the nucleus of the breed today.

The Gloucester Cattle Society is more than the mere revival of the Gloucestershire Cattle Society, despite the fact that today's Society sees itself as such. The situation has changed dramatically since 1919, and it would be a hopeless optimist who today tried to build a major dairy breed in a decade from a stock of seventy cows. Improbable then, it would be nearly impossible now for a 'new' dairy breed to find a foothold in the dairy industry, swamped today by the ubiquitous Friesian! Instead the present Society's primary aim is to ensure the survival of the breed. A Charitable Trust for the breed has been approved in principal, which would enable the Society to receive funds from outside sources towards the establishment of a permanent 'Home' for the Gloucester where this Charity would be legally bound to maintain pure Gloucester breeding stock for posterity. And the membership is fundamentally different too — the average herd size is under five animals, which means that there are thirty-five herd-owning members at the moment. This is healthy not only for the Society (its predecessor ended up as a handful of herds dependant on the dedication of their owners), but for the breed itself, for this spread of cattle considerably reduces the possibility of the whole breed being wiped out in the event of another epidemic. And furthermore many of today's breeders are not dependant commercially on their Gloucesters, which will give the breed time to recuperate and increase until numbers are such that commercial selection can take place without slaughtering the breed.

Amongst those using the Gloucester commercially today is Mr Frank Williams, of Hill Farm, Taynton. Mr Williams' eleven cow herd was founded on two cows bought at the Bathurst sale, and he is one of the few breeders aiming to develop the beef aspect of the breed, which is where, he believes, the future lies for the Gloucester. A 21-month old steer sold recently at Gloucester Market weighed 10½ hundredweight, and in this connection it is interesting to note that a bull tested by the Meat and Livestock Commission reached 1,202 lbs in 400 days.

For a century or more the occasional Gloucester has been used as a suckler cow in the Vale of Gloucester, and it has been suggested that the breed may have a future in multiple suckling; Mr and Mrs A. Parslow of Chapel Farm, Hartpury, have for some years been rearing upwards of nine calves a year on a Gloucester cow.

Milk records are more scanty. *Dymock Alkerton Princess 830,* one of the better-looking cows to emerge from Cold Aston, gave 802 gallons in her twelth lactation (1976); *Wick Court Molly 840,* perhaps the best cow at the Wick Court sale, has peaked at about 6½ gallons per day. Mr Chris Peachey, of Donkeywell Farm, Quenington (in the Cotswolds above Bibury), has for some years been using a Gloucester bull on his Friesian herd, and his highest half-bred yield to date is 1,200 gallons at 4.1% butterfat as a heifer. It is only fair to comment, however, that other cattle have been described as having very low yields; but to me it is a miracle that there is any milk left in the breed at all, for nobody has attempted to improve the yield of the purebred Gloucester since Colonel Elwes in the 1940's — and perhaps none before him since Long of Boddington in the eighteenth century! And there is a very real demand for Double Gloucester cheese made from the milk of the Gloucester, which is at present being met only by Charles and Monica Martell of Dymock, who sell it wholesale at £1.50 per pound. A cheese of their making, moulded from a nineteenth century cheese-press in the Gloucester Folk Museum and bearing the arms of William IV, was presented to Prince Charles when he visited the Three Counties Show in 1978.

Showing has been as actively encouraged by this Society as by its forebear, with much benefit to the breed. A number of cattle are shown each year at the Show and Sale of the Rare Breeds Survival Trust at Stoneleigh, but the breed's home showground is once again the Three Counties; classes were first booked there in 1974 when nine cattle were shown, and in 1975 the Miss Dowdeswells presented a silver cup to the Society for the Supreme Champion of the Show. One of the most successful

Royal Gloucester: *Wick Court Molly 840* and owner Eric Freeman meet Princess Anne at the Three Counties Show, 1976. *Gloucester Journal.*

*Bemborough Saul 848* 'Star' of the early years of the revived breed society. *Gloucester Cattle Society.*

breeders in the showring has been Mr Eric Freeman, of Little Cugley near Newent, who has won the Championship no less than three times in four years with the bull *Bemborough Saul 848. Saul* was saved from slaughter by Chris Peachey, who sold him to Freeman in 1973, since when he became one of the best known of all Gloucesters through his show success and through the quality of his progeny, today found throughout the breed. Freeman's herd was founded on two halfbred cattle he bought at a dealer's sale at Tetbury in 1971, since which time he has been buying every good Gloucester he could find and upgrading his crossbreds. His herd in 1978 numbered 40 cattle, far and away the largest in the breed. Freeman has also owned the only bull not of Wick Court descent (*Noent Napoleon Bigarreau 1000*), bred from black Bathurst Gloucesters that he traced down to Devon, and whose use will do much to improve the genetic quality of the breed.

Inbreeding is the major problem facing the Society today. Two animals are reputed to be of Colesbourne descent, and a handful of others were bred at Cold Aston; but the vast majority of today's Gloucesters are still pure Wick Court. A breed relationships chart was drawn up in 1976 by Ministry of Agriculture breeding specialist Ken Deebles to help the Society advise on matings, but inbreeding remains a problem because, to a certain extent, every breeder is his own expert and does not like being advised by someone else. Far be it from me to commit the same error, but it is essential that some of the cobwebs of mythology that still hang over the breed are dispelled before it's too late. Inbreeding causes infertility, calf mortality and decreased productivity, and these are proven facts; the Badminton herd may well have foundered and sunk through overuse of a stock bull in the early twenties (page 63). The genetic pool of the Gloucester is far, far too small to allow for selective 'in-and-in breeding', in our case the crossing of nice-looking animals regardless of their relationship. Breeders must go out of their way to select the right bull for their cows, and plan matings between cattle as little related as possible, for infertility is still all too prevalent in the breed. Semen is available from eight bulls at the moment, so there is plenty of choice.

Breeds develop, and certainly the Hereford of today, for example, is in many respects different from his eighteenth century ancestor; but this is no excuse for any breeder today to try experimental outcrossing to look for improvement. In view of the policies of Ralph Bathurst and, indeed, his father, it is questionable whether the breed today is indeed genetically the same thing as it was in 1919. Improvement must come from within and the breed must be kept pure until numbers are large enough for such outcrossing not to imperil the breed's survival. More co-ordination and co-operation between the breeders and their breeding policies is essential; perhaps the answer would be a centralised, voluntary breeding policy right across the breed.

Six years after the Wick Court Sale the Society is flourishing, and it now has over seventy members. Publicity has never been better, and in particular the herds of Charles Martell and Joe Henson have had wide coverage, both in the press and on television. In this connection tribute must be paid to Mr Henson, and to the phenomenal success of his Cotswold Farm Park over the last eight years, which without a doubt is the biggest single factor in the breed's popular success, and he has used his increasing fame to benefit the breed in a number of ways.

United we stand, divided we fall: witness Ralph Bathurst. If the desire to 'go it alone' can be suppressed, if personal ambitions can be forgotten, if it is realised that the Society — and thus the breed — is the sum total of its members, then the breed will survive. With cautious dedication and prudent breeding it might succeed.

# The Glamorgan Connection

Reference has already been made to the modest expansion of the Gloucester into Wiltshire and Dorset, and there is good evidence that the Gloucester also contributed to the early improvement of the Hereford; but the breed's expansion westward into Glamorgan was on a far different scale.

For some reason the nineteenth century agricultural writers, cribbing from their predecessors and lacing their accounts with generous helpings of fiction, believed without exception that the Gloucester was descended from the Glamorgan. The theory defeats logical explanation; for, whilst it is true that white cattle — with red ears — were to be found in parts of Wales until the seventeenth century, and that cattle were to be found in large numbers in seventeenth century Glamorgan, the finchback element almost certainly came from the east, in all probability with the red-brown colour, and not vice versa. Glamorgan farmers were importing cattle from Gloucestershire in the late seventeenth century and possibly earlier (page 16), and as late as 1814 the farmers of the Gower Peninsular referred to their original breed as 'our old blacks'. By the late eighteenth century, at any rate, the Glamorgan had become almost identical to the Gloucester, in terms of colour if not in conformation.

The Glamorgan emerges into documented history as a predominantly beef breed, with a nationwide reputation:

King George III — 'Farmer George' — had a team of Glamorgan oxen at Windsor, which he replenished annually. Glamorgans were to be found working on the Cotswolds, and fattening in Leicestershire, Warwickshire, Northamptonshire and Wiltshire. Steers fattened to 9½-11½ cwt — one monster reached 16 cwt — and cows up to 10½ cwt; but already the breed was on the wane in face of competition from the Castlemartin; it was slower maturing, and despite the excellent quality of the meat, on the whole the drovers found them delicate. And it should be remembered that these weights were for Vale-fattened cattle; on the hills the breed had already degenerated into 'mere pygmies', 2½-3½ cwt being the average size of a hill-bred cow. During the Napoleonic wars the Glamorgan farmers discovered that bread was more profitable than beef, and neglected to improve the breed at the time when it was crucial to do so. Not only was the breed superseded in its old English strongholds; once the demand for beef returned, Glamorgan farmers themselves turned to the 'new' breeds in a desperate effort to improve their own breed's productivity. The result was widespread out-crossing, at first with beef breeds — Longhorn, Devon and Hereford — but when these failed to inject improvement, a belated drive towards developing the Glamorgan as a dairy breed was tried; crossing with the Shorthorn did not succeed, although a cross with the Ayrshire was much more successful. There were also some attempts to improve the breed from within. One of the county's leading farmers, Evan David, of Radyr Court and Fairwater House, lamented the degeneration of his county's breed —

'There is one striking circumstance which I beg to notice, namely, that previous to the establishment of these various works (mining etc), this county was noted for its fine cattle. I

The Glamorgan: *Working Glamorgan Ox* by James Ward, R.A., c.1820. One of the oxen brought up regularly from Glamorgan for George III's Windsor farms. *Museum of English Rural Life, Reading.*

Glamorgan bull c.1889, bred by J.T. Davies of Pontlanfraith, Monmouthshire; the only known photograph of a Glamorgan. *R. Wallace, Farm Live Stock of Great Britain, 2nd. ed. 1907.*

have been informed by some of the most eminent graziers in Leicestershire and Warwickshire, that fifty or sixty years ago they regularly attended our farms, which were then supplied with an abundance of fine oxen, equal, at that time, to any in the Kingdom; but they had long ago ceased to do so, because of the infirmity of the supply, both in quality and quantity'.[35]

David was one of the handful of breeders who sought genuinely to preserve and improve the Glamorgan, and won twelve prizes for his stock at the Tredegar Show — his sideboard was 'loaded with the testimonies of the superiority of his cattle' — but his attempts at improvement petered out into crossbreeding. More dedicated were the Bradley brothers Edward and Christopher, who built up a fine dual-purpose herd at Treguff, near Cowbridge. The herd averaged four gallons a day, and their dairy character is testified to by the cow in Lows' justly famous painting; but their beef record was good too. One steer was fattened to 1,520 lbs at three years, and won the supreme championship for all breeds at Tredegar one year; in all the Bradleys won 60 prizes there. Unfortunately for the breed, the Treguff herd was sold in 1850, and the cattle dispersed and crossed out of existence.

The Improvers had failed. Morgan Evan's epitaph was the most poignant:

'A few energetic breeders rose to do battle for the cattle of their forefathers, and, although very great progress was made, and a fair standard of perfection at certain points was attained, it became impossible to stem the tide against the invaders. Three or four local breeders were prominent to the last, but death and other changes caused the last strongholds to give way, and we might almost say that the end has come'.[36]

One breeder who remained faithful was the extraordinary Dr William Price, of Ty Cletar, near Llantrissant. Price had a small dairy herd, descended from his father's at Pontypridd in the eighteenth century, and by the 1880's Price believed his cattle to be 'the only pure descendants' of the true Glamorgan breed. In 1884, the Duke of Beaufort's agent, on the look-out for good cattle to improve the ailing bloodlines at Badminton, induced him to part with a cow and a bull, and two more followed a year later. The remaining nine cattle presumably died out after his death in 1893. Price believed himself to be an arch-druid, and dressed in fantastic clothing to fit the part; he also pioneered cremation by winning a court case after burning the body of his son — Jesus Grist — on the hillside above Llantrissant. His career was altogether spectacular, and he is still remembered and revered in Wales today.

The last purebred Glamorgan is believed to have been sold in 1898, but the finchback continued to recur sporadically. One such cow was discovered and purchased by Baron Cromwell in 1926, who persuaded the Gloucestershire Cattle Society to register her as 'Glamorgan Breed Foundation Stock' in January 1927.

The Glamorgan is yet another example of a good breed that, through fashion and neglect, was allowed to disappear; and but for the dedication of the Dukes of Beaufort it is certain that the Gloucester would have gone the same way.

To the west, Pembrokeshire once boasted a breed of its own — the Castlemartin, most famous of all the old Welsh breeds, a hardy, early maturing black breed that was often in competition with the Glamorgan and usually came out the better. The breed was often finchbacked and sometimes dark brown too, which indicates that at one time the breed was much influenced by cattle from Glamorgan. The breed was incorporated into the Welsh Black in 1876, and besides imparting much of its beefing quality, is probably the source of the white-marked cattle that still crop up today in the Welsh Black, despite the denial of the breed society!

# The Jenner Connection

Cowpox, a mild form of a smallpox, seems to have been a disease largely restricted to Gloucestershire in the eighteenth century, and it is to this coincidence that the world owes vaccination (from the Latin *vacca:* a cow) and the ultimate eradication of smallpox, Dr Edward Jenner his fame, and the Gloucester breed it's most illustrious member, a cow, belonging to Mr Dean of Berkeley, called Blossom. Blossom gave the disease to Sarah Nelmes, one of Dean's dairymaids, and on 14 May 1796, Jenner culminated over twenty years of investigation (into why those who had had cowpox did not contract smallpox) by transferring serum from Nelmes's arm to that of an eight-year-old boy called James Phipps. The experiment succeeded, and Jenner became internationally famous, but he continued to live in Berkeley and to have strong connections with Gloucestershire: he even married a Kingscote. Neither was Blossom forgotten; after living out her days in honourable retirement in Berkeley, her hide was kept by Jenner and hung in his coach house. A suggestion that he should donate it to the British Museum was apparently ignored, and it wasn't until 1857 that the hide came to London, presented to St George's Hospital, where Jenner had studied, by his family. But Blossom couldn't escape from the Jenner cult, which began in his own lifetime, and no less than five horns are today attributed to her, no mean achievement even for a Gloucester. As late as 1896 hairs from her tail were up for auction!

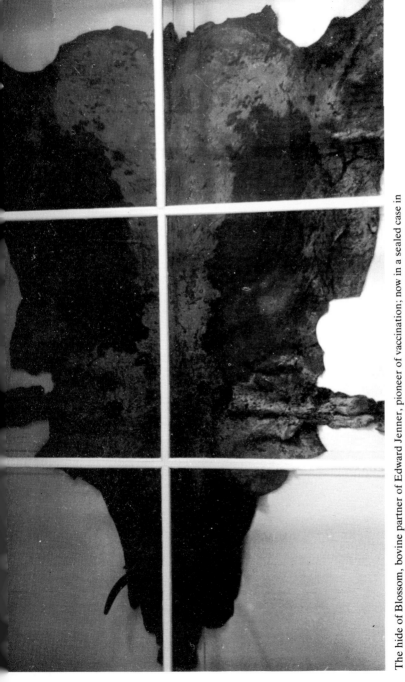

The hide of Blossom, bovine partner of Edward Jenner, pioneer of vaccination; now in a sealed case in the Medical School Library, St. George's Hospital, London. The horns are not original. *St. George's Hospital.*

# Bibliography

## Abbreviations

FW *Farmers Weekly*
GCL *Gloucester City Library*
GRO *Gloucester Records Office*
Glos. Jnl *Gloucester Journal*
GVA... *General View of the Agriculture of the County of . . .*
JB&WE *Journal of the Bath & West of England Agricultural Society*
JRASE *Journal of the Royal Agricultural Society of England*

## Periodicals

*Better Breeding* (1969)
*Farmer's Magazine* (1853)
*Gloucester Journal* (1776-82, 1818, 1842-3, 1896, 1920)
*Gloucestershire Notes and Queries* (1879-1914)
*Journal of the Royal Agricultural Society of England* (1844, 1863)
*Modern Farming* (1919)
*Monthly Review* (1789)
*Museum Rusticum* (1765)
*Times* (1943, 1965)
*Western Mail* (1927)
*Wilts. and Glos. Standard* (1925)

## Unpublished Material

*Gloucester Cattle Society Records* 1919-66, very generously given
to me by Mrs Margaret Smail, and now deposited with the

Gloucester Cattle Society, Laurel Farm, Dymock, Glos. The Minute Book, Accounts and 'personal files' on individual breeders are particularly useful.

*Gloucestershire Records Office,* Shire Hall Gloucester:
   *Fretherne Court Estate Sale Papers*, 1918-19 (GRO D 2299)
   *Badminton Estate Records*, Farming Accounts (from 1696) (GRO D 2700)
   *Quarter Sessions books*, 1746-52
   *Commonplace Book of Nathaniel Clutterbuck* (D 149/F13)

*Colesbourne Park Estate Records*, Estate Office, Colesbourne, Glos.
   Three important folders of correspondence, cuttings and photographs relating to the Colesbourne herd and the latter days of the Society

*Public Records Office*, Chancery Lane, London EC1
1871 Census Returns for Hardwicke and Haresfield; Bristol and Gloucester Port Books

## Published Sources

'Agricultural Returns for Great Britain', 1866, London 1867

Aubrey, J. 'Natural History of Wiltshire' ed. John Britton, London 1847

Ayres, R. 'Black Breeds were driven into the west' (letter, FW 2 February 1973)

Baron Dr. John 'Life of Edward Jenner' (2 vols, London 1827)

Bathurst, R.H. 'Vanishing Breeds' (letter, FW 8 February 1946)

Bathurst, S.H. seventh Earl 'Gloucestershire Cattle', *Morning Post* 17 January 1925

— 'An Experiment in breeding Gloucestershire Cattle'

— *Field* 22 November 1930

Bond, F.T. publicity leaflets 'Gloucestershire and cheese-making' 1908

— 'Gloucester Roundels', n.d.

— 'The dairy versus the slaughterhouse', n.d.

Boston, E.J. 'Jersey Cattle' (London 1954)

— 'Vikings may have spread the breeds' (letter, FW 9 February 1973)

Braend and others 'Genetic studies on blood groups in Icelandic cattle' *Sederat ur Hereditas* 1972

Bravender, J. 'Farming of Gloucestershire', J *RASE* 1856

'Buyers to preserve rare Gloucester cattle', *Citizen* 26 October 1972

Caird, J. 'English Agriculture 1850-51' (London 1852)

*Calendar of Sherborne House Muniments*, at Gloucester Record Office (1900)

Cardiff Farmer's Club *First Annual Report* 1842

Cheke, V. 'Story of Cheesemaking in Britain' (London, 1959)

'Chipping Sodbury', *Gloucestershire & Avon Life*, February 1976

Claridge, J. 'GVA Dorset' (London 1793)

Darell, Sir L. 'Ratcatcher Baronet' (London, privately printed 1952)

Davies, W. 'GVA South Wales' (London, 2 volumes 1814)

Davis, T. 'GVA Wiltshire' (London, 1794)

Davis, J.G. 'Cheese' (Edinburgh, 4 volumes, 1965-1976)

Defoe, D. 'Tour through the Whole Island of Great Britain' (London, 3 volumes, 1723-27)

Elwes, H.C. 'Awaiting Opportunity' (letter, FW 15 February 1946)

— 'Gloucestershire Cattle' in 'British Pedigree Cattle' (*National Cattle Breeder's Association,* 1947)

Evans, M. 'The Glamorgan Breed of Cattle' in J. Coleman (ed.), 'Cattle of Great Britain' (London, 1875)

Fleming, G. 'Animal Plagues' (London, 2 volumes, 1871-82)

Frith, B. 'The "Fun" that killed the Fair', *Citizen* Centenerary Supplement, 1976

Fullbrook-Leggatt, L. 'Anglo-Saxon and Medieval Gloucester' (Gloucester, 1952)

Gamgee, J. 'The Cattle Plague' (1866)

Garrard, G.A. 'Description of the Different Varieties of Oxen Common in the British Isles' (London, 1800)

Gloucester Cattle Society *Herdbook* (1975, 1978)

— *Newsletters* Autumn 1974, Christmas 1975, Spring 1977

'Gloucesters are back in the ring', FW 14 June 1974

Gloucestershire Cattle Society *Herdbook* (1920, 1922, 1923-5, 1927, 1930, 1935, 1940, 1945)

Grzimek, B. (ed.) 'Animal Life Encyclopedia' (Wokingham, 1972-75)

Hart, W.H. (ed.) 'Historia et Cartularium Monasterii Sancti Petrii Gloucestreii' (London, 1863-67)

Hartman, E. 'Extracts from the Court Rolls of Churchdown, with Norton, Hucclecote, Witcombe and Shurdington' (*manuscript* at GCL, no. 7568)

Hassall, C. 'GVA Pembrokeshire' (London, 1794)

Jenner Dr. Edward 'An inquiry into the causes and effects of the variolae vaccinae' (London 1798)

Jenkins, J.G. 'The English Farm Wagon' (University of Reading, 1961)

Lawrence, J. 'General Treatise on Cattle' (London, 1805)

Lawson, J. 'Practical Agriculture' (1827)

Lisle, E. 'Observations on Husbandry' (ed. Thomas Lisle, London, 1757)

Low, D. 'The Breeds of the Domesticated Animals of the British Islands' (London, 2 volumes, 1842)

Mackay, B. 'The Scandinavian Influence',*Ark* July 1974

— 'The Telemark Cline', *Ark* August and September 1975

Macdonald, J., and Sinclair, J., 'History of Hereford Cattle' (London, 1886)

MacGregor, A. 'The Breed with a Forgotten Past is given a new Future', FW 1 January 1973

Maddever, K. 'Double Gloucester' *Agriculture* August 1966

Marshall, W. 'Minutes of Agriculture' (London, 1778)

— 'Planting and Rural Ornament' (London, 2 volumes, 1796)

— 'Rural Economy of Gloucestershire' (Gloucester, 2 volumes, 1789)

— 'Rural Economy of the West of England' (London, 2 volumes, 1796)

Martin, W.C.C. 'The Ox' (London, 1847)

'Middlehorn' 'Gloucestershire Cattle: Four Years' Progress' in *Farmer and Stockbreeder Yearbook*, 1924

Mills, J. 'A Treatise on Cattle' (London, 1776)

Ministry of Agriculture and Fisheries 'British Breeds of Livestock' (London, 1910)

Moreau, S. 'A Tour to the Royal Spa at Cheltenham, or Gloucestershire Displayed' (Bath, 1783)

Morton, J.S. 'Farming of Gloucestershire', J *B&WE* 1864

National Milk Records, 1927

Nicholas, T.I. 'A Welsh Heretic' n.d.

Norwegian Red Cattle Association publicity handouts 'Norwegian Reds' n.d. c. 1970

— 'Black can be Red — at least in Norway', n.d. c.1970

'The Old Gloucestershire Breed of Cattle' J *RASE* 1909

'The Old Gloucestershire Cattle' *Country Life* 1 February 1908

'Old Gloucestershire Cattle: County Society Established' Glos. Jnl. 21 June 1919

Paterson, D.R. 'Pre-Norman settlement in Glamorgan', *Cambridge Archeological Association Journal* June 1922

Pitt, F. 'Gloucester Cattle, being an account of the herd of this ancient breed in the possession of Earl Bathurst' *Country Life* 18 December 1942

Popperwell, R. 'Norway' (1972)

Robinson, H.G. 'The Old Gloucestershire Cattle' *Country Life* 23 February 1935

Rudge, T. 'GVA Gloucestershire' (London, 1807)

Rudder, S. 'A New History of Gloucestershire' (Cirencester, 1779)

Simon, A. 'Cheeses of the World' (London, 1956)

Sinclair, J. 'History of Shorthorn Cattle' (London, 1907)

Smith, A.H. 'Place-names of Gloucestershire' (London, 4 volumes, 1964)

Smyth, J. 'Berkeley Manuscripts', (ed. Sir John Maclean, Gloucester, 3 volumes, 1883-85)

Stout, A. 'Three Centuries of London Cowkeeping' FW 18 August 1978

Stratton, J.M. 'Agricultural Records' (New Jersey, USA, 1969)

'Three Historic Breeds' *Field* 2 July 1959

Tomlin Smith, L. 'Itinerary of John Leland' (London, 6 volumes, 1909)

Trow-Smith, 'A History of British Livestock Husbandry to 1700' (London, 1957)

— 'A History of British Livestock Husbandry 1700-1900' (London, 1959)

Turner, G. 'GVA Gloucestershire' (London, 1796)

Vancouver, C. 'GVA Cambridgeshire' (London, 2 volumes, 1794)

Victoria County History, Gloucestershire (London, in progress)

Wallace, R. 'Farm Live Stock of Great Britain' (Edinburgh, 1907, 4th edition)

Warner, Rev. R. 'A Tour through the Northern Counties of England' (Bath, 2 volumes, 1802)

Windels, F. 'The Lascaux Cave Paintings' (London, 1949)

Youatt, W. 'Cattle: their breeds, management and diseases' (London, 1834)

Young, A. 'GVA Essex' (London, 2 volumes, 1807)

— 'Six Weeks' Tour through the South of England' (London, 1768)

## Notes

1. Anon., 'Three Historic Breeds', *Field* 2 July 1959.

2. William Marshall, 'Rural Economy of Gloucestershire' I (1789), pp. 213-5.

3. Robert Trow-Smith 'A History of British Livestock Husbandry' II (1959), p. 235.

4. John Smyth (of Nibley), 'Berkeley Manuscripts' I (1885, ed. Sir John Maclean), p. 366.

5. Trow-Smith I (1957), pp. 202-5; J. Macdonald and J. Sinclair, 'History of Hereford Cattle' (1886), p. 14, 25.

6. Edward Lisle, 'Observations on Husbandry' (1756, published posthumously), p. 267.

7. C. Ernest Watson, 'Cheesemaking in Gloucestershire', *Gloucestershire Life*, Spring 1941, pp. 59-60.

8. Smyth, 'Berkeley Manuscripts', I p. 127, 167; II 7.

9. Lucy Tolmin Smith (ed.), 'Itinerary of John Leland' II (1909), p. 63.

10. W.H. Hart (ed.), 'Historia et Cartularium Sancti Petrii Gloucestreii', III (1867), xcix, p. 295.

11. Gloucester Records Office 'Calendar of Sherborne House Muniments' (1900), p. 183.

12. 'Commonplace Book of Nathanial Clutterbuck', Gloucester Records Office, D 149/F 13.

13. Smyth, 'Berkeley Manuscripts', III 4, p. 89.

14. Quarter Sessions, Easter 1748 (22 March), Gloucester Records Office.

15. Marshall, 'Rural Economy' I p. 214, 216, 244.

16. *Ibid.*, I p. 212, II pp. 98-9.

17. Thomas Rudge 'General View of the Agriculture of Gloucestershire' (1807), p. 298.

18. Advertisement, *Gloucester Journal*, 6 February 1818.

19. William Marshall, 'Planting and Rural Ornament' II (1796), pp. 299-300.

20. Rudge, 'Agriculture of Gloucestershire', p. 282.

21. William Youatt, 'Cattle: their breeds, management and diseases' (1835) p. 149.

22. David Low, 'Domesticated Animals of the British Isles', (1842).

23. J.S. Morton, 'Farming of Gloucestershire', *Journal of the Bath & West of England Agricultural Society*, 1864. The figures are computed from the table on page 19, using the modern standard of two followers to one 'cow unit'.

24. James Caird, 'English Agriculture 1850-51' (1852), p. 45.

25. F.T. Bond, 'Gloucestershire and cheesemaking' (1908).

26. John Thompson, Badminton farm manager, quoted by Morgan Evans 'The Glamorgan Breed of Cattle', in J. Coleman (ed.), 'Cattle of Great Britain' (1887), p. 194.

27. 'The Old Gloucestershire breed of cattle', *Journal of the Royal Agricultural Society of England* (1909), pp. 415-9.

28. 'Old Gloucestershire Cattle: County Society Established' *Gloucester Journal*, 21 June 1919.

29. 'Middlehorn' 'Gloucestershire cattle: Four Years' Progress' in *Farmer and Stockbreeder Yearbook*, 1924, p. 98.

30. Gloucestershire Cattle Society *Herdbook* 1925, p. 5.

31. H.C. Elwes, 'Awaiting Opportunity' (letter in *Farmers Weekly*, 16 February 1946).

32. H.C. Elwes, 'Gloucestershire Cattle' in 'British Pedigree Cattle' (1947), p. 46.

33. R.H. Bathurst, 'Vanishing Breeds' (letter in *Farmers Weekly*, 18 January 1946.

34. R.H. Bathurst, letter of 20 March 1945, in Gloucester Cattle Society Records (Bathurst File).

35. Cardiff Farmer's Club *First Annual Report*, 1842, p. 16.

36. Morgan Evans, 'The Glamorgan Breed of Cattle', p. 191.

# INDEX

Alexander, Sir Claud 58
Alney Island, Glos. 15, 20
Ampney Crucis, Glos. 57
Andrews, S.C. 9
Artificial insemination 71, 78
Ashcurch, Glos. 29
Aurochs *see* Bos Primigenius
Ayrshire cattle 30, 71, 80

Badminton herd 16, 40, 43ff, 47, 48, 52, 58, 59, 63-4, 77
*Badminton Bentley 2* 59, 63
*Badminton Bentley's Smart I 244* 59, 60
*Badminton Jock I* 59
*Badminton Perfect II 175* 63
*Badminton Starlight 238* 55, 63
Bakewell, Robert 29-30, 35, 39, 41, 63
Barton Fair, Gloucester 20
Barton St. Gloucester 20
Bath, Somerset 24, 41
Bathurst, Ralph 65ff, 70-71, 78 *see also* Cold Aston, Ciren.
Bathurst, S.H. *seventh Earl* 52, 54-8, 59, 60, 65, 78 *see also* Cirencester, Ciceter
Beaufort, *Duchess of* (wife of tenth Duke) 63, 67
*Dukes of* 40, 43, 51, 83
*ninth Duke* 48, 51, 55, 59
*tenth Duke* 59, 60, 63 *see also* Badminton
Beckfield, Glos 29
*Bemborough Saul 848* 63, 77
Bentley, A.F. 53, 63
Berkeley, Glos. 18, 57, 84
castle 20, 41
*earls of* 14
Maurice (fl.1269) 19
Thomas (1281-1321) 19-20
Thomas II (1326-61) 20
estate 45
hundred 19
vale of 18, 23, 31, 34, 63
vicar of (seventeenth century) 23
'Black Gloucester' cattle 71, 77
*Blossom* 84
Blue Vinny cheese *see* Cheese
Boddington, Glos. 35-6, 75

Boddington Oak 38
Bond, Dr Francis 42-3, 47
*Bos Longifrons* 13
*Bos Primigenius* (Aurochs) 11, 13
Bradley, Edward and Christopher 82
Bristol 24, 41
Brookthorpe, Glos 47
Brown, Samuel 40
Buckle, James 35n, 38
Butter 20

Cadbury's Dairy, Frampton-on-Severn 72
Caen, Normandy 19
Cam, Glos 62
Cambridgeshire 25
Canada 53
Canley, Warks. 29
Carolina, U.S.A. 24
Carter, Christopher 47
Castlemartin cattle 16, 26, 80, 83
Cattle Plague *see* Rinderpest
Channel Island cattle 45 *see also* Jersey, Guernsey
Cheese:
Blue Vinny 25
Cheddar 42, 43
Cheshire 24
Gloucestershire 18, 19, 20, 24-5, 33, 34, 41-5
Wiltshire Loaf 25
Chelt, river (Glos.) 36
Cheshire 24, 28, 63
Chipping Sodbury, Glos. 20
Churchdown, Glos. 21-22
Ciceter herd 55, 59
*Ciceter Czar 235* 63
*Ciceter Rubra A17* 55
Ciren herd 67, 70 *see also* Cold Aston
Cirencester Park 52, 66, 70
Clutterbuck, Nathaniel 23
Cleeve Hill, Glos 35n
Codrington Sir Gerald 48
Cold Aston, Glos. herd 70, 71, 74, 75, 77,
Colesbourne Park, Glos. 51, 54, 65
herd 52, 67, 77
*Colesbourne Bluebell* 54, 55

Colling Brothers (Robert and Charles) 41
Coln St Aldwyns, Glos. 57
Cotswold Farm Park, Guiting Power, Glos. 78
Cotswold Sheep 18
Cowbridge, Glams. 82
Cowpox 84
Cripps, Sir Frederick 57, 67
Cromwell, Robert *fifth Baron* 57, 83

Darell, Sir Lionel 46-7, 62 *see also* Fretherne
Dartmoor, Devon 25
David, Evan 80-2
Davies, F.A. 53
Dean, Mr — 84
Deebles, Ken 77
Devon 23, 77
Devon cattle 12, 22, 25, 30, 80
Dodington, Glos. 48
Dorington, Sir John 47-8
Dorset 25, 71, 77
Double Berkeley *and* Double Gloucester, *see* Cheese: Gloucestershire
Dowdeswell, Alexandra and Ella 72, 73, 75
　Eric 62, 67, 72
　Robert 62, 63
Dowdeswell Cup 75
Droving 16, 19, 22
Ducie, Earl 41
Dursley, Glos. 62
Dusgate, George 66, 67
Dymock, Glos. 73, 75
*Dymock Alkerton Princess 830* 75
Dynevor, Lord 55-7

Elmore, Glos. 62
Elwes, Col. H.C. 51, 54, 60, 65-6, 67, 75
Essex 25, 33
*Eva 10* 70

Fairwater House, Glams. 80
Falfield, Glos. 51
Faygate, Sussex 65
Fitzhamon, Robert 13-14
Foot-and-Mouth Disease 58
Forthampton, Glos. 28, 65

Frampton-on-Severn, Glos. 40, 72
Freeman, Eric 63, 72, 75
Fretherne, Glos. herd 46, 50, 51, 54, 57, 59, 62
Friesian cattle 22, 30, 36, 45, 71, 73, 75
Frocester, Glos. 34
*'Fussy'* family of Gloucester cattle 72

Gazzard, Martin 57
George III 80
Glamorgan 12, 15, 16, 25
Glamorgan cattle 15, 26, 46, 53, 57, 79ff
Glastonbury, Somerset 13
Gloucester 13, 19, 20, 52, 66
　Abbey 21
　Dairy School 42, 43
　Folk Museum 75
　Market 22, 34, 74
Gloucester cattle *main headings only*
　Colour patterns, evolution of 12-13, 21-3, 47
　Crosses with other breeds 9, 31ff, 52, 59 *see also* Bathurst, Ralph and S.H.
　Description 8-9, 36-7, 48-50
　Expansion outside Gloucestershire 8-9, 36-7, 48-50
　For beef production 30, 47, 74
　　draught 25, 30
　　milk production 9, 19, 30-1, 53-4, 70, 75 *see also* Cheese: Gloucestershire suckling 74
　Rearing and management 21, 32-4, 39-40, 45-6, 71
　Societies 46-8, 51ff, 58-59, 65-8, 71, 73ff
Gloucester cheese *see* Cheese: Gloucestershire
Gloucester Dairy Association 42, 47
Gloucester Old Spots pigs 24
Gloucester, Vale of (geology) 18
Gloucestershire 12, 16, 23, 25, 26, 29
Gower peninsular, Glams. 79
Gresley, Sir Thomas 29
Guernsey cattle 48
Guiting Power, Glos 72

Hampshire 24
Hardwicke, Glos. 34, 47, 50, 51, 58
Haresfield, Glos. 34

Harrisson, Lionel 59, 66
Hartpury, Glos. 75
Henson, Joe 72, 73, 78
Hereford cattle 9, 14, 15, 22, 25, 30-1, 38, 78, 79, 80
Herefordshire 23
Hewlett, Richard 40
Hicks-Beach, Sir Michael 57
  Ladies Susan and Victoria 57, 66
Hook, Richard 45
Horsley, Glos. 23

Jenner, Dr Edward 84
Jersey cattle 48

King, Peter 72
Kings' Board (medieval cheese market) 20
Kingscote herd 40, 41
  family 84
  Sir Thomas 40-1
Kirklevington, Yorkshire 41

Ladyswood Pansy 190 54
Lancashire 29
Lascaux caves, France 11, 13
Leather 20
Lemon & Parker Cup 52, 54
Leonard Stanley, Glos. 34, 40
Lincoln Red cattle 12, 52
Lincolnshire 12, 28
Llantrisant, Glams. 46, 82, 83
Lloyd-Baker, G.E. 46, 47, 51, 58, 59 see also Hardwicke
London 24, 34, 41
Long, Henry 35-8 and note 75
Longhorn cattle 15, 29-30, 31, 33, 35, 38, 39, 43, 80
Lutterworth, Warks. 57
Lyme Regis, Dorset 18
Lypiatt Park, Stroud, Glos. 47

Martell, Charles 73, 75, 78
  Monica 75
Milk Marketing Board 54
Misterton Colour Seargent 631 57-8
Minchinhampton, Glos. 18, 19
Monmouthshire 15, 23
Montgomeryshire 12

National Cattle Breeder's Association 66, 67
Neave, John 72
Nelmes, Sarah 84
Newent, Glos. 73, 77
Newnham, Glos. 22
Noent Napoleon Bigarreau 1000 77
Normande cattle 14
Norse influence 14-15
Northamptonshire 80
Norway 14
Nympsfield, Glos. 63

Old Gloucester see Gloucester cattle
Oxfordshire 30

Parslow, A. 75
Pathenaise cattle 14
Peachey, Chris 75, 77
Pembrokeshire 16, 26, 63
Phipps, James 84
Pinckney, Wilts 53
  herd 54, 57
Pontypridd, Glams. 83
Powell, Hon. Edward 53
Price, Dr William 46, 82-3

Quenington, Glos. 75

Radyr Court, Glams. 80
Red Poll cattle 70, 71
Rinderpest (disease) 28-9, 41
Rollright, Oxon. 30

St. Aldwyn's, Earl 67
St. George's Hospital, London 84
Salt Lake City, U.S.A. 53
Sandhurst, Glos. 37
Saul, Glos. 46, 62
Savage, Major A.E. 72
Scudamore, Lord 14
'Severn Valley Dairy Produce Company' 42
'Severnside' (landrace cattletype) 12ff
Sharpness, Glos. 57
Sherborne, Dorset 25
Sherborne, Glos. 21
Shetland cattle 15
Shorthorn cattle 40, 41, 51, 52, 57, 59

Shows and Showing:
   Bath & West of England 52, 53
   Berkeley Hunt 52
   Rare Breeds, Stoneleigh 75
   Royal 50, 52
   Three Counties 52, 54, 55, 75
   Tredegar 82
Slimbridge, Glos. 34
Somerset 12
Staffordshire 29
Stonehouse, Glos. 34, 43
Stroud, Glos. 47
Suffolk 52
Suffolk Dun cattle 33
Surrey 25
Sussex cattle 12, 22
Sutton St. Nicholas, Herefordshire 9

Taynton, Glos. 74
Tetbury, Glos. 45, 77
Tidenham, Glos. 19
Tormarton, Glos. 48
Tortworth, Glos. 39, 41
Totton, Hants. 53
Treguff, Glams. 82

Vaccination, discovery of 84

Wagon, hoop-raved 16, 25-6

Warwickshire 80, 82
Webb, Thomas 58
Webster,—— of Canley 29
Webster, W.B. 35-6n
Wellington St., Gloucester 20
Welsh Black cattle 52, 83
Welsh cattle 22 *see also* Castlemar
   Glamorgan and Welsh Black
West Indies 24
White Park cattle 55-7, 65
Whiteshill, Glos. 72
Whitminster, Glos. 34, 73
Wick Court, Saul, Glos. 62 72ff
*Wick Court Ella 836* 72
*Wick Court Gloucester* 72
*Wick Court Molly 840* 75
Wickwar, Glos 39
Williams, Frank 74
Williams, Stanley 51, 57
Williamsburg, U.S.A. 24-5
Wiltshire 12, 24, 25, 67, 77, 80
Woodlands House, Hants. 53, 57, 59,

Yate, Glos. 48
Yorke, Vincent 65
Yorkshire 46
Young, Willie 72-3

Zoomorphism in farm wagons 25-6